Harper & Row Design for Reading   # FROM NEAR AND FAR

by Mabel O'Donnell

Copyright © 1972 by Harper & Row, Publishers, Inc.
All rights reserved.
Printed in the United States of America.

Standard Book Number 06-516006-1

Some of the material in this book was previously
included in a book published under the title
From Faraway Places, copyright © 1966,
Harper & Row, Publishers, Incorporated

HARPER & ROW PUBLISHERS

New York   Evanston

San Francisco   London

1817

ACKNOWLEDGMENTS

Grateful acknowledgment is made to the following authors and publishers who granted permission to reprint these selections:

"Marco and the Donkey Cart," an adaptation of BRAVO MARCO! by Pauline Priolo. Text copyright © by Pauline Priolo; pictures copyright © 1963 by Betty F. Peterson; translation copyright © 1963 by Parnassus Press. Adaptation approved and reprinted by permission of Parnassus Press, Berkeley, California.

RAMON MAKES A TRADE by Barbara Ritchie, an adaptation. Text copyright © 1959 by Barbara Ritchie; pictures copyright © 1959 by Earl Thollander; translation copyright © 1959 by Parnassus Press. Adaptation approved and reprinted by permission of Parnassus Press, Berkeley, California.

"Kobo and the Wishing Pictures," an adaptation of KOBO AND THE WISHING PICTURES: A STORY FROM JAPAN by Dorothy W. Baruch. Copyright © 1964 by Charles E. Tuttle Co., Inc., Tokyo, Japan. Adaptation approved and reprinted by permission of Charles E. Tuttle Co., Inc., Rutland, Vermont.

GOOD LUCK DUCK by Meindert DeJong, an adaptation. Text copyright © 1950 by Meindert DeJong; pictures copyright © 1950 by Marc Simont. Adaptation approved by the author. Reprinted by permission of Harper & Row, Publishers, Inc., New York.

"The Peddler of Ballaghadereen," an adaptation from THE WAY OF THE STORYTELLER by Ruth Sawyer. Copyright © 1942, renewed 1970 by Ruth Sawyer. Adaptation approved and reprinted by permission of The Viking Press, Inc., New York.

"Kobi, the Herdboy," an adaptation from KOBI, A BOY OF SWITZERLAND by Mary Marsh Buff and Conrad Buff. Copyright © 1939 by Mary and Conrad Buff. Published by The Viking Press, Inc., New York. Adaptation approved by the publisher. Reprinted by courtesy of Conrad Buff.

WINGS AGAINST THE WIND by Natalie Savage Carlson, an adaptation. Copyright © 1955 by Natalie Savage Carlson. Adaptation approved by the author. Reprinted by permission of Harper & Row, Publishers, Inc., New York.

"Why Spiders Hide in Dark Corners," an adaptation from THE ADVENTURES OF SPIDER by Joyce Cooper Arkhurst; illustrated by Jerry Pinkney. Text copyright © 1964 by Joyce Cooper Arkhurst; pictures copyright © 1964 by Barker/Black Studio, Inc., Boston. Adaptation approved by the author. Reprinted by permission of Little, Brown & Company, Boston.

The pronunciation system and key are taken from The Thorndike-Barnhart Dictionary Program. Copyright © 1968 by Scott, Foresman and Company, Glenview, Illinois.

CONTENTS

Illustrations: Dick Cody, Muriel and Jim Collins, David Cunningham, Beatrice Darwin, Fernando DaSilva,
Tom Hill, Herb Kane, Carl Kock, Charles Mikolaycak, Tak Murakami, George Suyeoka

Design: Bonnie Baumann, Brian Bourke

Home from the North Woods

Helping Yourself with New Words
Picture Dictionary

canoe

doll

Indian

road

Words You Can Get by Yourself

or	whiz	hot	dark	backward	round
north	whizzing	spot	darkness	upward	sound
				forward	
				homeward	
eat	drive	let us	cap	late	ride
seat	driver	let's	map	later	riding
shadow	sun	fellow	rub	sleepy	wood
shadowy	sunny	yellow	rubbing	sleepier	wooden
pile	made	old	broken	get	list
mile	shade	hold	broke	bet	mist
	shaded				
	tree-shaded				
gave	keep	hop	cry	book	loud
brave	deep	hopped	cried	booklet	aloud
had	men	ready	loud	safe	forgot
glad	ten	already	proud	safely	forgotten
word	all	wood	farm	soon	old
world	wall	stood	arm	sooner	older

Two Words Make One Word

blacktop   treetops   sideways   Springfield   crossroads

handwork   woodland   upturned   long-lost   understand

wayside   Greenfield   nighttime   somewhat

Let the Sentences Help You

1. Stop the car when you see a stop sign.
2. One of those boys is Sam. Which one is it?
3. My country is the U. S. A.   countries
4. A minute is 60 seconds.
5. I have written 3 letters to you.

Glossary

A mer i can (ə mer′ə kən), one belonging to the U.S.A.

an ces tor (an′ses tər), your father, grandfather, great-grandfather, and so on.

An ge lo (än′jə lō), a boy's name.

as ton ish (əs ton′ish), to surprise. **as ton′ished**

be hind (bi hīnd′), at the back of.

be tween (bi twēn′), in the middle.

birch bark (bėrch′bärk), the bark of a birch tree.

de scend ant (di sen′dənt). You are your father's and mother's descendant.

dis tance (dis′təns), a place far away.

ex plain (eks plān′), to tell why or how a thing is done. **ex plained′**

fam i ly (fam′l ē), a father, mother, and children.

guess (ges), to suppose without really knowing.

It a ly (it′l ē), country.

lead (lēd), to show the way.

point (point), to show with the finger. **point′ing**

real (rēl), so; true; not made up.

re al ly (rē′əl ē), so; truly.

sick (sik), not well; ill.

ver y (ver′ē), greatly; much.

vil lage (vil′ij), a little town.

watch (woch), to look with attention; to be on the lookout.

cap, fāce, cāre, fär; let, bē, wėre; it, īce; hot, ōpen, ôrder; voice, house;
cut, pu̇t, tülip, ūse; th, thing; ҭн, then; zh, garage; ə stands for *a* in about,
e in angel, *i* in cabin, *o* in wagon, *u* in suppose

Vacation Almost Over

It was a hot, sleepy afternoon in late summer. A car came whizzing along a blacktop road in the north woods. Spots of sunlight came and went in the darkness under the trees. The shadows of late afternoon danced across the road. Now and then a crow flew upward to ride the wind out over the treetops. There was only the low sound of the tires on the road and a boy's voice from inside the car to break the stillness.

"But, Dad, you said we would. This is almost our last chance. We'll be home tomorrow. You can't go back on your word. You just can't!"

Something was wrong. Anyone looking at Mark Waters could tell that. What was it that he wanted so <u>very</u>, very much? What was it that he was afraid he was not going to get? He boosted himself <u>forward</u> on the <u>seat</u> and turned <u>sideways</u> to look out the window.

Mr. Waters, in the <u>driver's</u> seat, looked puzzled about something. He waited a minute before answering.

"I know! I know!" he said then. "I'm sorry about it, too. We seem to have taken the wrong road. Every other time when I've been here, there have been <u>Indians</u> in every town I've come to. But there are no Indians around anywhere today. I agree we're having bad luck. What can I do about it? Tell me that."

"Let's go back and start all over again on another highway! It won't take too long. How about it, Dad? Look at the road map. Come on! Be a good fellow!" teased Mark. "We can make up time later on. Please, Dad, please!"

"Not on your life," said Mr. Waters. "Do you want us to get to Springfield too late to find a good place to stay for the night? Think of the good times you've had since we left home on our vacation. Remember the prize you got for that big fish. Think of those things. Then plan on seeing Indians when you come back again next summer."

When a fellow is as disappointed as Mark was, it's hard to keep from showing how you feel. He was sick and tired of riding. Why was it that a good vacation always had to end up with a tiresome ride home? He sat back in his seat and looked down at the floor.

Time went by. The car rounded one
turn and then another and left the dark,
shadowy woods behind it. Now the road,
all hot and sunny, tumbled down a long
hill between yellowing fields that went
on and on to the edge of the sky.

A lark called from meadow grasses, but
Mark didn't hear it. He just sat there,
rubbing his eyes and growing sleepier
by the minute.

It was only when Janet called from the back seat that Mark forgot to be sleepy.

"Look, Mark! A car coming from the left! Another coming away off there to the right! There must be another road up ahead. Keep your fingers crossed. We may not be out of luck after all."

As it turned out, Janet was right. At the <u>crossroads</u>, on the road to the left, was a <u>wooden</u> marker with the words:

Mystery Lake   3 <u>miles</u>
Indian Shops and <u>Handwork</u>

"Three miles! Only three miles!" Mark almost shouted, as his dad slowed the car and turned left.

Time passed. Then ahead of them they could see in the distance the blue waters of Mystery Lake. Before long the road turned and ran along the water's edge to the Village of Woodland Hills at the head of the lake.

It was a lovely little village of white houses and tree-shaded streets. People seemed to be everywhere, people who had come here for their summer vacations.

15

Most of the streets ended at the water front and at the shops to be found there. In an important place all its own was a shop with a big <u>sign</u> over the door <u>which</u> read:

Indian Trading Post
Come and Buy

Mark was out the door almost before his dad had time to stop the car. He was out so fast that he forgot to leave behind him the baseball he was <u>holding</u> in his hand. No time to think about baseballs now! There, on an <u>upturned</u> box in front of the shop sat an Indian boy about as old as Mark.

Mark had always liked Indians. He liked everything he had read about them in books or had seen on TV. Here was his chance to talk to an Indian boy. A <u>real</u> boy just like himself!

"Hi, there!" Mark called in a friendly voice. "What's your name?"

For just a minute the Indian boy
didn't answer. His eyes were on the
baseball in Mark's hand. In another
minute he jumped down from the box.
What was this on the upturned box
behind him? A BIRCHBARK CANOE!
Had he made it himself? Was that what
Mark wanted to buy? Was that what he
had to have?

The dark eyes of the Indian boy lighted
up. Mark could see them shine. If his
smile was not so big as Mark's grin, his
lips did turn up at the corners.

"Hi, there! That yours?" he asked,
pointing to the baseball in Mark's hand.

"Hi, there! That yours?" answered
Mark, pointing to the birchbark canoe.

Then as if the questions were a big
joke and needed no answer, the two boys
started to laugh.

"I'm Mark Waters. What's your
name?" Mark asked once again.

"Sam Woods," laughed the Indian boy.

Now you know how it is with boys. Once they start to talk, they become good friends in no time. Mom could go inside the shop to get an Indian basket. Janet could look for an Indian <u>doll</u>. Dad could entertain himself as best he could. Mark didn't have to look for anything. He knew what he wanted. He pointed to the sign up over the door, then to the birchbark canoe on the upturned box, then to the baseball he was holding in his hand.

"Trade! Want to tr . . .?" asked Sam, with a grin on his face as big as Mark's.

"Trade!" <u>broke</u> in Mark before Sam had stopped talking. "You <u>bet</u> I will!"

So trade they did. After that the two boys walked down to the water's edge, chattering away like <u>long-lost</u> friends.

There was one question Mark had to have answered. Why was the lake called Mystery Lake? Here is the answer as Sam told it to Mark.

At times in November, <u>mists</u> cover the lake in the early mornings. No one can see the water. Sometimes, so the story goes, the faces of the Indian <u>Braves</u> who once lived by the lake can be seen in the mist. They come back, so people say, to tell that the winter ahead will be a good one. If their faces can't be seen, snows will be <u>deep</u> and the winter will be a cold and hard one.

"Did you ever see them?" asked Mark, with wonder in his voice.

"Last year! I think so!" answered Sam. "Why do the Indian Braves come back? How do they know what the winter will be like? That's the mystery of Mystery Lake."

Why, at that minute, did Mark's dad
have to call, "Get a move on, Mark!
We're going!"

While Mark made for the car, Sam ran
in at the door of the Trading Post. In
a minute he was out again, holding
something in his hand.

"For you, Mark!" he shouted. "It tells
all about it!"

Mark <u>hopped</u> out of the car again,
while his dad looked on, too <u>astonished</u>
to say a word.

"Thanks, Sam! Thanks!" <u>cried</u> Mark.
"I'll see you next summer. Maybe!"

Once back in the car to stay, Mark sat holding up a booklet for Mom and Janet and Dad to see. On the cover it said, "The Story of Mystery Lake."

Once again the car whizzed along the hot, sunny highway. With the birchbark canoe on the seat beside him, Mark read aloud from the booklet the story of the Indian Braves.

Time went by. The sun was going down when at last the roofs of Springfield could be seen in the distance. It had been a long and tiresome day. Everyone was glad when Dad pulled into a gas station at the edge of town.

"Ten gallons will do it," he said from the open window. "Then please tell us the best place to stay for the night."

Talking Things Over

The next morning the car started <u>homeward</u> along roads which the <u>family</u> knew very well. They had left the north woods miles behind them. No chance of seeing Indians this morning. It was just a good morning to ride along, <u>watch</u> for stop signs, and take things easy.

Mark sat daydreaming the time away. In his dream he saw the mist covering Mystery Lake and in the mist the faces of the Indian Braves. He sat up with a start when his dad said, "By the way, Mark, who were the first <u>Americans</u>?"

"The first? The VERY first?" asked Mark, looking a little astonished at that question. "Were they the Indians?"

"Right you are," said his dad. "When the first white man came to this big country of ours, the Indians were already here. They may have come from some other country, too. Most people think that they did. But the important thing to remember is that they got here first. So they were the first Americans. Some of them were the ancestors of that boy you saw at the Trading Post. That is a big word—ancestors. What do you know about it?"

"Oh, our grandfathers, and great-grandfathers, and great-great-grand-fathers, and people like that are our ancestors. Am I right?" asked Mark.

"Smart boy!" said his dad, grinning down at him.

"And OUR ancestors came from another country," broke in Janet. "The first ones to come over stayed here, and they became Americans, too. Is that the way it was?"

"Let's say that you're right as far as you go," smiled her mom.

"They became Americans, but not first Americans," said Mark. "They got here too late for that. By the way, Dad, Sam is an Indian boy, but he can't be a first American. He isn't old enough for that. What does that make him anyway?"

"Of course he isn't old enough, Mark. But he is the descendant of the first Americans, and that is something to be proud of. Something you can never say for yourself! Do you understand what I am talking about?" asked Mr. Waters.

"I think I do," answered Mark.

For a minute or two there wasn't a sound out of Mark. Then he popped forward, pointing his finger at his dad.

"Say, Dad," he cried. "How about this idea. Am I your descendant?"

"I guess you are at that," laughed his dad. "I guess that's what you are."

A great big grin covered Mark's face from ear to ear.

"Then how about this?" he cried. "You must be my ancestor."

Mom, on the back seat, laughed loud and long, and Dad joined in. Only Janet saw nothing to laugh at.

"Oh, YOU!" she said to Mark. "You have to be an old, old man before you are an ancestor. Daddy isn't that old."

"Good for you! Stick up for me!" said her dad between laughs. "You are right in a way, Mark, but I don't like the idea. I don't want to be your ancestor or anyone else's for a long time to come. Put that idea out of your head."

"OK!" said Mark, with a grin that was bigger than ever. Then he whispered so that only Dad could hear, "But you are my ancestor and you know it."

"How about this, Mark?" called Janet. "I know a good riddle. What is it you can never be if you live forever?"

"I bet I know!" shouted Mark. "A FIRST AMERICAN! By the way, Dad, do you think Sam is real proud of being a descendant of first Americans?"

"If I were an Indian, I would be VERY proud," said Mr. Waters. "It's my guess that Sam feels the same way. Since you can never be a first American, Mark, why not be a good one?"

"OK!" said Mark, still grinning away to himself. "I may think about it."

Noontime came at last. Mark and Janet were sick and tired of riding. They were glad when Dad stopped for lunch at a <u>wayside</u> stand outside <u>Greenfield</u> Village.

"I can eat ten hamburgers," shouted Mark, as he hopped from the car.

After lunch the family rested for a while in the <u>shade</u> of the big trees, talking to the people who ran the stand. Of course they had to see Janet's Indian doll and the birchbark canoe.

It was the middle of the afternoon before the roofs of Redwood City could be seen in the distance. When the family came to Spring Street, no one was around anywhere on this hot summer day. Only Windy Chase's yellow dog, Spot, followed the car into the garage, barking and wagging his tail.

By nighttime the house was in order again. No one would have known that the family had been away. Mom and Dad were hard at work, taking care of the cards and letters which had come while they were away. Janet and Mark were safely in bed.

All at once Mark called, "Come here a second, Dad. I've got to tell you something. I've just got to."

"Now what?" asked his dad from the doorway. "You should be asleep, young man."

Then do you know what that Mark said?

"Thanks for a grand vacation," he whispered. "Good night, ANCESTOR!"

Before his dad could pull his ear or do a thing about it, Mark ducked deep down under the covers.

A Map and an Idea

Some ideas are not good for much and are soon <u>forgotten</u>. Some ideas stick in your head and make you uneasy. Then all at once you know what to do about them. That's the way it was with Mark.

On the day before school opened, Mr. Waters was about to step into his car on his way to work. Mark ran out of the house to head him off.

"Say, Dad, do you know where I can get a map of the <u>world</u>?" he cried. "I just came up with a keen idea."

"Well, now," answered Mr. Waters, "there is one on the <u>wall</u> of my office. Someone gave it to me. It's two maps in one, but it's a map of the world, all right. What do you want it for?"

"You won't tell if I let you in on something, will you?" asked Mark.

"Of course not! Out with it!" said his dad, still holding the car door open.

When the secret was told, Mark's dad looked surprised and pleased, too. He <u>stood</u> for a minute or two, thinking things over.

"Not a bad idea," he said with a smile. "Not bad at all! I just wonder what Miss Winters is going to think about it."

"I will find out tomorrow!" shouted Mark, as he ran in to breakfast. "Don't forget that map, Dad."

A day or two later Mark left for school early in the morning. Not one of the Spring Street gang saw him go. Under his <u>arm</u> was a map of the world.

By the time the other boys and girls came in at the door, the map was up on the wall and Mark, all important, was standing beside it. In two places on the map were cards with Mark's name upon them.

"What's this all about? What's your name doing up there?" asked John Sun-Yee, turning first to Mark and then to Miss Winters for an answer.

"It's Mark's idea, and a good one," said Miss Winters. "So suppose we let him tell what this is all about."

When Mark explained why the Indians were the first Americans, everyone but Mark and Miss Winters opened his eyes in surprise. FIRST Americans! That was a new way of looking at things.

"My dad's ancestors came from this country," explained Mark, pointing to the place on the map where he had put the first name card.

"My mother's ancestors came from here," Mark went on, pointing to the second card. "My ancestors became Americans, but not first Americans, and you know why."

"Now this is what I was thinking," Mark said next. "Any one of you who finds out where his ancestors came from can put his name on that country, just the way I did. Maybe you will need two cards, as I did."

"By the time we are done, there will be someone's name on every country in the world!" cried David Mays. "Boy, oh, boy, will that be something!"

"Not on every country," laughed Miss Winters, "but it will be fun to find out how many countries will have names on them. Leave room for my name, too."

"What am I supposed to do?" asked Angelo, with a puzzled look on his face. "My ancestors didn't come. Just my family and myself!"

"But your dad IS your ancestor!" cried Mark. "Your mother is, too. You ask them and see. So put your name on the country they came from. That is where it belongs."

By the time school was over for the day, everyone who did not already know had something important to find out when he got home.

Maybe you who are reading this story have something important to find out, too. If, like Angelo, you were born in another country, you know that country's name. But if you were born in the U.S., from what country or countries did your ancestors come? Do you know?

Did You Really?

Angelo was not the only one in the room who had been born in another country, but he was the first one to say so. This was a new idea. Some of the boys and girls looked at him in surprise. He didn't look any different. He didn't act any different.

You know how one good idea can lead to another. No sooner had Angelo put his name up on the country of Italy than everyone started in to ask him questions.

What is Italy like? What did you do to have fun? And so on and so on.

Maybe you think that Miss Winters should have put a stop to the questions. Well, she didn't. She asked one or two questions herself.

At first the questions made Angelo uneasy, and all he said was, "Just like over here! What do you think?"

Then all at once his face lighted up.

"I know one good story," he said, with
a big grin. "It happened to a boy who
lived in my village in Italy."

Everyone sat still to listen.

You who are reading this story did not
hear a word of Angelo's story, and that
is too bad. So in the following pages you
will find it. Not in just the way he told
it, but in the way I found it <u>written</u> down
in a book.

Daydream

I sat and looked at a map today,
Until all at once I was up and away,
High in the air
And out over the sea,
To the faraway places
I've longed to see.

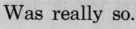

Someday when I'm <u>older</u>
And have grown <u>somewhat</u> bolder,
Oh, then I will go,
And then I will know
If that wonderful daydream
Was really so.

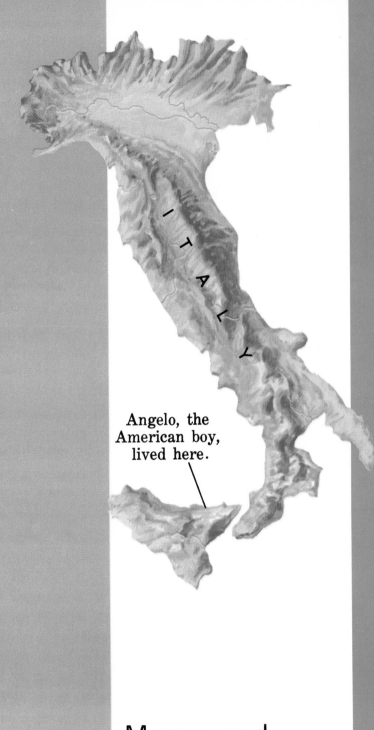

I T A L Y

Angelo, the
American boy,
lived here.

Marco and
the Donkey Cart

Picture Dictionary

bagpipes

bundle

cart

cottage

donkey

garden

mirror

music

shafts

shepherd

toes

vegetables

Words You Can Get by Yourself

dust	proud	bright	feel	dance
dusty	proudly	brighter	wheel	dancing
		brightly		

coat in	new	care	farm	astonish
goat skin	newly	stare	farmer	astonishment
goatskin		stared		
		staring		

how	side	hid	love	loud
crowd	aside	hidden	loving	loudly
			lovingly	

old	wise	book	own	weed
oldest	wisest	shook	owner	feed

slipper	disappoint	leg	eat	cap
slip	disappointment	beg	eaten	strap
slipped		begged		

may	listen	village	know	cry
gray	fasten	villager	knowing	try
			knowingly	tried

not	well	will	miss	if
trot	fell	willing	misses	lift
		willingly		lifted
		unwillingly		

happy	gave
happily	wave

Two Words Make One Word

firewood	hilltop	workman
onlooker	onto	whenever

43

Let the Sentences Help You

1. You must <u>finish</u> this job before you go.   finished

2. Two is <u>more</u> than one.

3. Help me to <u>carry</u> this big basket.   carried

4. Red, blue, and green are <u>colors</u>.

5. I cannot <u>use</u> this broken skate.
   It is of no <u>use</u> to me.
   use (ūz)   use (ūs)

6. I want to work and <u>earn</u> money.

7. He is too <u>lazy</u> to do any work.   lazier

8. I will give <u>each</u> of you a book.

9. The street gets wet when it <u>rains</u>.
   When I drive my pony, I hold onto the <u>reins</u>.

10. Did you <u>hear</u> me?
    I <u>heard</u> every word you said.

11. You pull the wagon
    while I <u>push</u> from behind.   pushed

12. This room is 15 <u>feet</u> long.
    See the new slippers on my <u>feet</u>.

Glossary

be lieve (bi lēv′), to think that something is so.

bra vo (brä′vō), a cry or shout to show that something is well done.

bray (brā), the noise made by a donkey. **brayed**

budge (buj), to move.

ex claim (eks klām′), to cry out in surprise.

ex claimed′

gath er (gaᴛʜ′ər), to bring into one place. **gath′ered**

har ness (här′nis), the straps and other things that fasten an animal to a wagon or cart.

live ly (līv′lē), full of life.

Mar co (mär′kō), a boy's name.

mar ket place (mär′kit plās), a place where things are sold.

mer ri ly (mer′ə lē), in a happy way.

mer ry (mer′ē), happy.

oats (ōts), a grass used as feed for animals.

pas ture (pas′chər), a grassy field.

rea son (rē′zən), the cause.

Ser a fi na (sär ə fē′nə), the name of a donkey.

spar kle (spär′kl), to send out sparks of light.

spar′kled   spar′kling

stub born (stub′ərn), wanting to have one's way.

tem per a men tal (tem′pər ə men′tl), changing one's way of feeling and acting often and without reason.

tie (tī), to fasten something with a cord or string so that it will not come undone. **tied**

to ward (tôrd), in the direction of.

tune (tün), a piece of music; a melody.

wom an (wu̇m′ ən), a lady.

Zi Peppi (zē pep′i), a man's name.

cap, fāce, cãre, fär; let, bē, wėre; it, īce; hot, ōpen, ôrder; voice, house;
cut, pu̇t, tülip, ūse; th, thing; ᴛʜ, then; zh, garage; ə stands for *a* in about,
e in angel, *i* in cabin, *o* in wagon, *u* in suppose

Grandfather and Marco

The donkey cart was <u>finished</u>. There it stood in the <u>dusty</u> road in front of the little white <u>cottage</u> where Marco lived with his grandfather.

When I tell you that Grandfather's ancestors and their descendants had lived in this same white cottage for <u>more</u> than 200 years, then you will know how old the house really was.

Now in the early morning sunlight, Marco stood <u>proudly</u> beside Grandfather. Together they looked down in wonder at the little cart. Their eyes were shining, and the pleased look on their faces showed how happy they were.

Could it be that they had made this beautiful cart all by themselves? It was big enough to <u>carry</u> ten times as many <u>bundles</u> of <u>firewood</u> as Marco and Grandfather could ever carry on their backs in one day.

Every morning Marco and Grandfather walked up the dusty country road to the woods outside the little village where they lived. All morning long they <u>gathered</u> the dry branches from under the trees and <u>tied</u> them into bundles. Then, with the bundles on their backs, they walked the long road into town and sold the bundles of firewood in the <u>market</u> p<u>lace</u>.

The Wonderful Cart

The early morning sunlight made all the different <u>colors</u> of the donkey cart <u>brighter</u> than ever.

Marco had helped with the painting. It was he who had painted the two long <u>shafts</u> and the two wooden <u>wheels</u>. But only Grandfather could paint pictures like those on the sides and back of the wonderful cart.

In one place on the side of the cart were some dancing puppets. They looked and acted just as the puppets had done in the puppet show that had come to Marco's village the summer before.

In still another place on the same side, men and boys were dancing merrily. They were dancing in a market place very much like the one in Marco's own little village.

On the back of the cart a shepherd stood on a hilltop, looking down upon his sheep and lambs in the green meadow below.

On the other side of the cart were the two pictures Grandfather liked best. In one, some boys and girls were singing merrily. In the other, two older boys played on their bagpipes.

No wonder it was those two pictures that Grandfather liked best. He loved music. When the afternoon shadows were growing longer and the day's work was done, Marco would take out his goatskin bagpipes and play one tune and then another. Grandfather never tired of listening and always asked for more. Boys and girls forgot their play to come and dance to the merry music.

An old shepherd from the hills outside the town had sold the bagpipes to Grandfather. It was from this same shepherd that Marco had learned to play one merry tune and then another.

Today, as he stood by the side of the road, Marco was not thinking of bagpipes. The only thing he could think about was the beautiful cart.

"Someday I will be driving you," he whispered, as he climbed up and sat down on the newly painted seat.

What? No Donkey?

By this time the boys and girls from the rest of the village had gathered around the cart, <u>staring</u> at the bright colors and the beautiful pictures.

The <u>woman</u> from the cottage next door left her seat beside her doorway to walk over and tell Grandfather what a wonderful <u>workman</u> he was.

<u>Farmers</u> on their way to market stopped to <u>stare</u> in <u>astonishment</u> at the little cart. Never had they seen a cart so bright and so beautiful.

One farmer had a great basket on his back, piled high with the vegetables he had grown in his garden. The basket was so big that he could hardly carry it.

"Oh, for a cart like that!" he seemed to be saying, as he rested his basket on the low wall beside him.

All the onlookers agreed that there had never been a cart so beautiful.

Then all at once a voice from the crowd called out, "Where is the donkey to pull the cart?"

Other voices joined in. "Yes, tell us. Where is the donkey?"

For a second or two, not a sound came from the crowded street. Everyone was waiting for Grandfather's answer, but no answer came.

Zi Peppi, the farmer with the great basket on his back, stared at Grandfather in surprise.

"Have you gone to all the work of making this cart with no donkey to pull it?" he asked in astonishment.

Still Grandfather said nothing. Marco knew why. He remembered Grandfather's words while they were working on the cart.

"Of what use is a cart without a donkey to pull it? How people will laugh at us! From now on, there is nothing but hard work ahead for us, Marco. We must earn money to buy a donkey before we can use this cart."

For almost a year Grandfather had been putting aside money to buy a donkey. He had hidden the money away in an old sock in one corner of the white cottage. Now, when he needed it most, the money was gone.

Some of the money had been used to buy the goatskin bagpipes. Some to buy the two wheels for the donkey cart! Grandfather could not make those wheels all by himself. Some money had been used to buy the bright-colored paints he had needed to paint the pictures.

The rest of the money had gone for a bag of oats and a bright red harness for the donkey still to come. Everything was ready. All they needed now was the donkey.

Just this morning Marco and Grandfather had talked things over. From now on they would make more trips to the woods. More trips, more firewood! More firewood, more money! Then, at last, a donkey all their own!

Now, while the crowd waited for his answer, Grandfather ran his hand <u>lovingly</u> over the side of the donkey cart. He smiled up at Marco on the newly painted seat.

"Soon," he said to the waiting crowd. "Soon Marco and I will have our donkey."

An Astonishing Idea

Zi Peppi stared at Grandfather. He could not <u>believe</u> what he was hearing.

"A donkey!" he <u>exclaimed</u>. "Where in the world will you get one? Until you do, your cart will stand here in the sun while you and the boy break your backs carrying firewood."

All at once someone in the crowd laughed and called out, "Why don't you give them a donkey, Zi Peppi?"

"I! I give them a donkey?" Zi Peppi exclaimed in astonishment.

"Yes," another voice answered. "Why not make them a present of <u>Serafina</u>, that hard-working donkey the puppet show people sold to you last summer?"

Everyone laughed <u>loudly</u>, and Grandfather and Marco joined in.

Everyone in the village knew about Zi Peppi's lazy donkey that would not leave the pasture to do any work. She could not be sold because anyone who wanted to buy her could not get that donkey to move.

When anyone asked about her, Zi Peppi's face turned very red. Then Zi Peppi would start right in to explain.

"She was lively enough the day she came home to the farm," he would say. "From that day on, she has become lazier and lazier. Now she wants to do nothing but eat."

Now an old white-haired man stepped forward from the crowd. He was the oldest and wisest man in the village. His eyes sparkled as he looked at Zi Peppi with a knowing smile.

"Have you had any luck in finding someone to buy Serafina?" he asked. "Have you had any luck at all?"

Zi Peppi <u>shook</u> his head.

"No!" he said. "No luck at all!"

"Then why not give her away?"

"I cannot give her away. Did I not pay hard-earned money for her?" answered Serafina's <u>owner</u>.

"Aren't you tired of <u>feeding</u> a lazy, do-nothing donkey that takes life easy while you are doing her work?" asked the wise old man.

"You are right!" Zi Peppi exclaimed. "Each day I grow more tired of it. Each day Serafina grows more lazy and stubborn."

"Silly man!" called a woman's voice from the crowd. "Why do you let a donkey tell you what you must do? Be smart! Don't let a donkey get the better of you. Give her away. Then you can buy what you want with the money it takes to feed her."

Zi Peppi's face turned redder than ever. Everyone in the crowd was making fun of him. For a minute or two Zi Peppi stood thinking things over.

"All right! It's a bargain. Serafina is yours," he said at last, turning to Grandfather. "All I ask in return is a ride to market every morning with my basket of vegetables."

"Bravo, Zi Peppi, bravo!" called one voice and then another. "Bravo! Bravo!"

Thank You, No!

"Thank you, no!" cried Grandfather. "What good will a lazy donkey do me?"

Marco agreed. They could not feed a do-nothing donkey. Then all at once a wise idea popped into his head.

"Take her, Grandfather!" he shouted.

Grandfather shook his head. "She won't work for us, Marco, when she will not work for her master."

Marco <u>slipped</u> down from the seat, <u>disappointment</u> written all over his face. He could not let this happen.

"Please, Grandfather," he begged. "Who knows? Maybe Serafina isn't really lazy and stubborn, but—."

Marco was thinking of another little donkey in the village. Sometimes that donkey sat and brayed and would not work. At other times no donkey would work so hard as she. Temperamental! That is what everyone said she was.

"Maybe Serafina is temperamental, too," Marco said to Grandfather. "Maybe she is just temperamental and needs someone who understands her."

Everyone laughed loudly.

"Well," said Grandfather with a smile. "We will give Serafina a chance and see. Zi Peppi's farm is on our way to the woods. So it will not be out of our way to stop there when we go to gather our firewood."

Marco remembered that Serafina loved to eat.

"I will get some oats to take to Serafina," Marco said to Grandfather.

"Don't trouble yourself," laughed Zi Peppi. "She has already eaten today. Enough for two hard-working donkeys!"

"Then I've something else she may like," said Marco, as he ran back into the little white cottage.

A minute later he was back with a beautiful red harness on his arm. The mirrors on the harness straps sparkled brightly in the sunlight.

The wise old man looked first at the bright red harness and then at Marco.

"Don't be surprised if Marco leads Serafina right out of your pasture," he said, turning to Zi Peppi. "Some boys have a way with donkeys."

Zi Peppi looked as if he did not believe a word the man was saying.

"Go out to my pasture and show what you can do," he said to Marco. "The next time I see that do-nothing donkey, I hope she has this harness on her back and is pulling this cart."

Serafina

"Good luck!" everyone called, as Marco and Grandfather started up the road to Zi Peppi's farm.

There in the pasture was Serafina, the gray and white donkey. She seemed very friendly, rubbing Marco's hand with her nose as he patted her.

"I have nothing to feed you. Why didn't I bring you some oats after all?" said Marco softly.

"Take your time. Go easy," whispered Grandfather, as he handed the harness to Marco.

Slowly Marco placed the harness on Serafina's back. The donkey stood very still to let him <u>fasten</u> the straps. Before Marco knew how it happened, he was finished. He could not believe that it had been so easy.

There stood Serafina, all harnessed and ready to go. The red of the harness was just the right color, and all the little mirrors sparkled in the sunlight. Marco's eyes sparkled as brightly as the mirrors.

"See if she will go with you to the open gate," whispered Grandfather.

"Come, Serafina, come," said Marco softly, as he pulled on the reins.

Serafina heard him. He knew that she did. Up went her ears, but she did not budge. Marco pulled a little harder. Still Serafina did not budge.

"It's no use," said Grandfather. "Come Marco. We must gather firewood."

It was a sad and disappointed Marco who let go the reins and stared at the donkey. When Serafina looked at him, he knew that she liked him. Then why was she so temperamental?

"We can't give up, Grandfather," he said. "Think of the money we can earn if she will only go with us."

Grandfather would wait no longer. While Marco pulled once more on the reins, Grandfather walked out of the pasture gate on his way to the woods.

"Time is flying," called Grandfather, as he walked up the road. "There is firewood to be tied into bundles."

"Just a while longer! Please!" Marco called in return. "Maybe we can think of something else Serafina wants from us. I have it, Grandfather. I know what it is. Serafina has a beautiful harness. Isn't it right that she should have a beautiful cart to go with it?"

Grandfather laughed loudly. "How can we show her the cart if she will not go with us?"

"We can bring the cart here!" cried Marco. "Please, Grandfather, please!"

"Here!" exclaimed his astonished grandfather. "Of all the wild ideas!"

"But when Serafina sees the cart, she will come with us," begged Marco.

Grandfather turned around. "Come on then if you must have your way. Everyone in town will laugh at us."

So back Grandfather and Marco went to their own white cottage.

Soon the <u>villagers</u> saw Grandfather between the shafts of the donkey cart, pulling it slowly up the hot, dusty road while Marco <u>pushed</u> from behind.

One woman laughed loudly. Then others joined in, calling across the road to one another and joking about the silly things some people were doing.

At last Marco and Grandfather were back at the farm, tired and hot from their long walk in the sun.

On and Off Again

Grandfather and Marco stopped just outside the pasture gate. Inside the gate Serafina stared <u>knowingly</u> at the little two-wheeled cart.

"Look, Grandfather! She loves it!" exclaimed Marco.

All at once Serafina started to <u>bray</u>. They patted the donkey. They talked to her. They did their best to lead her out the gate and up to the cart. Serafina went right on braying, but she would not budge.

"Enough is enough!" exclaimed Grandfather, when he could stand no more of this nonsense. "I will gather firewood, and you, Marco, take that harness off that stubborn, do-nothing donkey."

Marco did not say a word. He was sorry now that he had made Grandfather take that long, hot walk in the sun to bring the cart to the pasture.

Marco turned to look at the donkey, that was still braying. Grandfather would be gone for a while. Would Marco have time to <u>try</u> something else?

Without knowing why he did it, Marco jumped up <u>onto</u> Serafina's back. The donkey turned her head to stare at him. He patted her head and poked her sides with his <u>toes</u>.

Up went Serafina's ears. The donkey <u>carried</u> him at a fast <u>trot</u> around the pasture. Marco could not believe that this was really happening.

"Bravo!" shouted Marco. "If only Grandfather were here now! You are a lively one. You just need someone who understands you."

Marco's words made Serafina trot faster and faster. Now if only—. He turned Serafina's head <u>toward</u> the open gate. Just ten more <u>feet</u>, and they would be out the gate and up to the little cart.

Ten more feet! Then what happened?

All at once Marco was flying backward off Serafina's back. He <u>tried</u> to hold on to her tail as he <u>fell</u> down to the hard ground. He had a bad, bad fall.

Marco jumped to his feet, as mad as mad could be. By this time Serafina was back in the middle of the pasture, braying loudly.

"What's wrong with you?" shouted Marco. "Any other donkey would be glad to be harnessed to a cart as beautiful as this."

Serafina just went on braying.

Music for Serafina

Slowly and <u>unwillingly</u> Marco started to take the beautiful little red harness off Serafina's back. As he was doing so, his eyes lighted upon the picture of the dancing puppets on the side of the wonderful cart. He walked around to the other side, and there he saw the two boys playing their goatskin bagpipes.

Marco's eyes sparkled. Those pictures gave him an idea. Maybe! Now, maybe!

Back to the village he ran, faster than he had ever run before.

When he returned, Grandfather was throwing a bundle of dry branches into the cart. He looked at Marco in astonishment.

"What are you doing out here with those bagpipes?" he exclaimed.

"I am going to play for Serafina," Marco answered.

"Silly boy!" exclaimed Grandfather. "Who ever heard of music for a donkey? Put an end to this nonsense. There is work to be done."

"But, Grandfather," begged Marco. "Serafina belonged to the puppet show we saw last summer. The people who ran the show played bagpipe music. Maybe that is what is wrong with Serafina. She misses all the music."

Grandfather shook his head to show that he did not believe a word Marco was saying. Not one word!

Marco looked over at Serafina. The donkey had stopped braying and was eating grass. He started to play on his goatskin bagpipes.

As soon as Serafina heard one of the tunes Marco had learned from the shepherd on the hilltop, her ears went up. She <u>lifted</u> her head to listen. She didn't move until the music ended.

Then Serafina walked right out the gate and around to the front of the cart. Then she turned around and backed up between the shafts. There she stood, all ready to be harnessed.

"She likes it! She likes it!" Marco
shouted, laughing merrily. "Serafina
likes music, as you do Grandfather. Now
she wants to carry us home."

Grandfather cried out in astonishment,
"If I did not see it with my own eyes, I
would not believe it."

In a minute or two, Serafina was
harnessed. The wheels of the cart
started to turn. Grandfather and Marco,
up on the seat, were on their way back
to the village.

Bravo, Marco!

As they were riding along, Marco and Grandfather came upon Zi Peppi on his way home from the market place. Marco pulled on the reins to stop Serafina. At first the farmer was so surprised that he could hardly talk.

"How did you get that lazy donkey out of my pasture?" he asked at last.

"Remember what the wise old man told you," answered Grandfather. "Boys do have a way with donkeys. Marco played his bagpipes for her. Serafina is not lazy. She just likes music."

"Music!" cried the astonished voice of Zi Peppi. "Is that what did it? And I believed that the man who sold her to me was just joking when he told me that a little music before breakfast was all Serafina needed to make her work <u>willingly</u> and <u>happily</u> all day long."

Grandfather laughed a merry laugh.

"He should have told you what would happen if she did not get her music," he said to Zi Peppi. "He should have told you that without music she would not budge. We will be by in the morning to carry you and the basket of vegetables from your garden to the market place. Until then, good-by!"

The farmer grinned. "The joke is on me, but I stick to my word. Serafina is yours from now on."

As Grandfather and Marco came riding
into the village, boys and girls playing
in the street saw them coming. They
crowded around the cart, shouting, "They
have their donkey! Marco and his grandfather have a donkey for their cart now!"

Windows opened, and surprised faces
looked out. Doors flew open, and people
crowded out into the dusty road.

"Bravo, Marco!" cried all the boys and
girls.

"Bravo! Bravo!" cried all the rest of
the villagers.

Marco and Grandfather <u>waved</u> to everyone along the way. Grandfather's face was one big happy grin.

"Play, Marco," Grandfather said. "Play a tune for Serafina while I hold the reins."

So Marco played on his bagpipes while dancing feet followed the wonderful cart down the village street. Marco looked down happily at Serafina. In the hot afternoon sunlight each mirror on her harness was <u>sparkling</u> brighter than it ever had before.

Temperamental

A minute ago I was happy,
But now I am feeling sad.
I no sooner seem to be happy
Than something makes me mad.

A while ago I was laughing.
All at once I started to cry.
Whenever I'm good,
I want to be bad,
And I don't know the reason why.

Maybe you can tell me the reason.
Do you know why I'm acting this way?
When I tried to explain
To my mother,
This is all I found to say.

I GUESS I'M TEMPERAMENTAL.

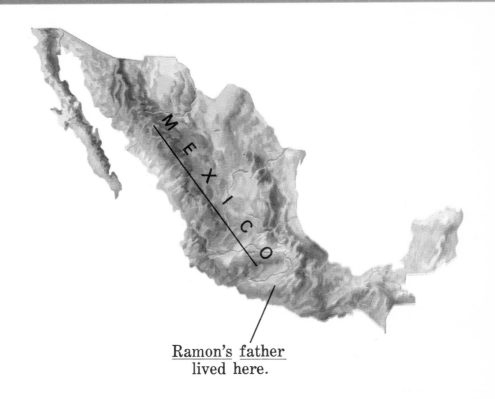

Ramon's father
lived here.

Ramon Makes a Trade

Helping Yourself with New Words
Picture Dictionary

feathers

mountain

parrot
(par′ət)

serape
(sə rä′pē)

Words You Can Get by Yourself

grandfather	lead	told	peep	show
father	leader	retold	steep	bow
				bowl
wag	all	buy	careful	car
rag	stall	buyer	carefully	jar
ragged				
pet	great	page	pony	shine
pot	greatest	cage	ponies	fine
potter				finest
pottery				
hot	6	leave	much	glad
hat	six	weave	such	gladly
	mix	weaver		
	mixed			
old	20	hop	wake	weed
fold	twenty	drop	awake	deed
folded		dropped		indeed

pipe   push   word   kind

stripe   pusher   worth   kindly

Two Words Make One Word

storyteller   schoolroom   businessman   lookout   mountaintop

Let the Sentences Help You

1. A dog has a tail.
   A story is sometimes called a tale.

2. When I see a friend, sometimes I say "Hi," and sometimes I say "Hello."

3. The dogs ran out through the gate.

4. What do you think of my plan?
   I thought of it in bed last night.

5. May I eat a piece of cake?

6. I had to crawl through the window   crawled
   to unlock the door.

7. My dad said that it would rain.
   He was right. His words came true.

85

Glossary

a bove (ə buv′), in a higher place; over.

ac cord (ə kôrd′). To do something of one's own accord means to do something without being asked.

add (ad), to join or put together.

blan ket (blang′kit), a soft covering to keep one warm.

bur ro (bėr′ō), a donkey.

busi ness (biz′nis), trading; buying and selling.

cen ta vo (sen tä′vō), a piece of money used in Mexico.

ex cite (ek sīt′), to stir up one's feelings. **ex cit′ed ex cit′ing**

hand some (han′səm), good-looking.

jin gle (jing′gl), to make a noise like little bells. **jin′gled**

ma ma (mə mä′), mother.

Mex i co (mek′sə kō), a country south of the U.S.

or ange-col ored (ôr′inj-kul′ərd), reddish yellow, like an orange.

pa pa (pə pä′), father.

plat form (plat′fôrm), a floor above the ground.

poor (pür), in need of help.

Ra mon (rä mōn′), a boy's name.

riv er (riv′ər), a stream of water.

San di no (sän dē′nō), a man's name.

screech (skrēch), to cry out in a high voice. **screech′ing**

tears (tirz), drops of water coming from the eyes.

vis it (viz′it), to go to see someone; to make a call on someone.

---

cap, fāce, cāre, fär; let, bē, wėre; it, īce; hot, ōpen, ôrder; voice, house; cut, pu̇t, tülip, ūse; th, thing; ŦH, then; zh, garage; ə stands for *a* in about, *e* in angel, *i* in cabin, *o* in wagon, *u* in suppose

The Storyteller's Story

Do you know how to play a game called "Follow the Leader"? Someone in Miss Winters' schoolroom in Redwood City did. No sooner had Angelo's story come to an end than Ramon said in an excited voice, "I know a story as good as that. It happened to my father. His name is Ramon, too.

"My father used to live here, but I never did," he said, running up to the map on the wall and pointing to the country of Mexico. "He said that he lived not far from an old, old village at the foot of a mountain. Do you know what else he told me? In that village there used to be a man who was the village storyteller. Every market day he sat in the shadow of a tree in the market place and told some old tales, or stories, about Mexico. Everyone crowded round to listen because those tales were so exciting.

"Once when he was a boy," Ramon went on, "something happened to my father. Something good that he remembered for a long, long time! Then he came to this country and became a man and forgot all about it. Years later, when he went back for a <u>visit</u>, the storyteller was still there, and what do you know about this? One of the tales he was telling in the market place was my father's story."

Here is his father's story, not as Ramon <u>retold</u> it, but as it was told by an old storyteller in an out-of-the-way village at the foot of a mountain in Mexico.

Down, Down the Mountain

The road down the mountain was long and <u>steep</u>, but the little gray <u>burro</u> did not miss a step. All that could be seen of him was his legs, his tail, and his two long ears. His two bright eyes were peeping out from between the many-colored <u>bowls</u> that were fastened to his sides and back.

Down and around, and then down again at a slow trot, went the little gray burro. Down to the old, old village at the foot of the mountain!

Ramon's father, in his old <u>ragged</u> <u>serape</u>, walked beside the burro, holding the reins and taking care to see that no bowl fell and was broken. Behind the burro walked Ramon's mother, and behind Ramon's mother walked Ramon.

In his hands the boy carried the beautiful bowl that he had made all by himself. His hands were on the bowl, but his eyes were on the many holes in the road in front of him.

It would not do to fall and break the bowl it had taken so long to make. Nothing must go wrong until he and his father and mother were safely at their stall in the market place.

"Ramon," his father called back to him. "Do you want me to put your bowl in our stall and try my best to find a buyer for it? For a boy, it is a bowl to be proud of."

"Thank you, no, Papa!" said Ramon.

For the first time Ramon lifted his head and took his eyes off the road to look at the orange-colored bowl he was carrying so carefully.

"You are beautiful," he seemed to be saying. "But how are you going to look when you stand beside Sandino's jars and bowls in the market place? Maybe then you will not seem so beautiful."

Sandino, Ramon's father, was the best potter in the village. One of the best potters in all Mexico! Ramon knew this. All the jars and bowls in the family stall in the market place were supposed to be made by the master potter himself and by no one else.

On market days people crowded around Sandino's stall, shouting, "We have come to buy a water jar made by the greatest potter of them all."

At this minute Ramon was thinking, "People will not want a bowl made by just a boy. For that reason Sandino will have a hard time finding a buyer. Maybe he cannot find a buyer at all."

Then a very wise idea popped into Ramon's head.

"If no one will buy my bowl," he shouted, "I will trade it for something I want, and I know just what that something is going to be."

"You are a wise boy, Ramon," said his mother. "That is a good way to do business at the market. Not many people there have money, but all of them have goods to trade. What is this thing for which you will trade one orange-colored bowl?"

Ramon smiled, thinking of that something that would soon be his.

"It is a secret, Mama," he said, "and I cannot tell a secret."

In the Market Place

Once at the market, Ramon left Mama and Papa at their stall and pushed his way between the crowds of people. Everyone was moving from stall to stall, looking things over before buying.

All at once, <u>above</u> the noise of shouting people and braying burros, he heard a loud and <u>screeching</u> voice.

"<u>Hello</u>! Good-by! Hello! Good-by!" screeched the voice above all the other sounds in the market place.

Ramon laughed loudly. He stood high on his toes, trying to see over the heads of the people around him.

"I hear you, Mr. Parrot," he said, talking to himself. "I'm coming to get you in trade for this bowl I made. I will carry you home in your cage, and before long you will learn to say many things besides 'Hello' and 'Good-by.' I will keep you forever, and everyone will know that you are Ramon's pet."

Ramon pushed ahead toward the place from which the screeching voice was coming. At times he could hardly budge because of the crowd.

Once he stopped of his own accord. He was passing a merry-go-round. He saw the wooden ponies, each one of them a different color. Boys and girls, hair flying in the wind, were riding merrily round and round, laughing and calling to one another.

Under the big round <u>platform</u>, Ramon
could see three boys about as big as himself. They were pushing hard and
kicking up dust with their feet as they
worked to keep the merry-go-round
turning round and round.

Ramon liked the merry-go-round very
much, but he must pay a <u>centavo</u> to ride,
and he didn't have a centavo. Maybe if
business was very good, Papa would give
him a centavo at the end of the day.
Now he had something more important
to do than to ride a merry-go-round.

The Stall of the Bird Cages

Ramon moved along until at last he popped out of the crowd in front of the stall of the bird cages. There were ever so many cages with nothing in them. There was just one cage with a little parrot inside. How beautiful the little bird was, with its bright green feathers and its long green tail.

"Good day!" screeched the parrot.

It turned its head and looked right at Ramon with one shining eye.

The man who made the cages was
paying no attention to the screeching
bird. He was looking at Ramon's
beautiful orange-colored pottery bowl.

"That is a fine bowl you have there,"
he said. "It is so fine that I think it
must be one made by Sandino, the potter."

Ramon pushed his big hat far back on
his black hair. A proud look came into
his eyes as he stood there.

"Sandino, the potter, is my father," said Ramon proudly. "But I made the bowl myself on my father's pottery wheel. I mixed the color for it, too."

Things were going better than he had hoped. Maybe it would not be hard, after all, to trade his wonderful bowl for the little parrot in the cage.

"For the cage and the parrot I will trade my fine bowl," he said to the man.

How the man laughed! He laughed until tears came into his eyes. Then he put his hand on Ramon's head.

"You do not understand business," he said with a smile. "The cage took me long to make. It was a hard job to catch the parrot in the woods. It was a long time before the parrot learned to say 'Hello' and 'Good-by.' The bowl is a fine bowl, but it would take six bowls as fine as this before I would trade the cage and the little parrot."

Ramon looked at the bowl. The warm orange color of it did not seem so beautiful to Ramon as it had before.

The man's eyes were kind as he looked down at Ramon's unhappy face.

"What I would really like to have," he said, "is one of your father's green water jars. I would strap it on my burro's back and carry water from the <u>river</u>. For one of the green jars, I will trade the cage and the parrot."

"Thank you," said Ramon. "I will see what I can do."

The Serape Weaver

Ramon turned away without much hope. His father would never give one of the handsome green jars for a cage with a screeching bird inside. His father was not such a bad businessman as that.

What Sandino, the potter, really needed was a new serape in place of his ragged one. He could use it as an overcoat on cold days and as a blanket on cold nights. For such a serape, Ramon's father would gladly give a water jar.

Once again Ramon looked down at the orange-colored bowl. It looked more beautiful than ever. Maybe the serape weaver would think so, too. Maybe he was looking for a handsome bowl just like this. Would he trade one of his serapes for the bowl? Then Ramon would trade the serape with his father for a green water jar. Then he would take the jar to the bird-cage man and—.

Once again Ramon made his way through the crowds in the market place. His bright eyes were on the lookout for the weaver. At last, high above his head, he saw a pile of folded serapes moving slowly through the crowd. He waved and called to the weaver, who did not have a stall but was carrying the folded serapes on top of his head.

The weaver laughed loud and long when Ramon asked him to trade one bowl for one serape. He would not do it.

"Not that it isn't a fine bowl!" said the weaver, as he saw Ramon's unhappy face. "It is a well-made bowl, and I would like to have it."

He stood there a minute, thinking.

"Here is what I will do," he said then. "I will take, in trade for one serape, your fine bowl and <u>twenty</u> centavos. Twenty centavos is not much money, I know. But then, the bowl is such a beautiful orange color, and I want it because of that."

"Thank you," said Ramon. "I will see what I can do."

<u>Poor</u> Ramon! How was he going to get twenty centavos in order to trade —

twenty centavos and the bowl
for the serape;

the serape for a green water jar;

the green water jar
for the cage with the parrot?

Once Again the Merry-Go-Round

Ramon walked away with tears in his eyes. There was no one who could help him. There was nothing he could do to help himself. Why, he had never in all his life had twenty centavos at one time.

"Good-by!" called the screeching parrot from its faraway stall.

"Good-by, Mr. Parrot!" answered Ramon, so softly that no one but himself could hear. "Wait for me in your cage. Someday I will make six beautiful bowls and <u>mix</u> the colors for them, too. Then I will come for you."

Before long Ramon was back beside the merry-go-round. The ponies were still going round and round. Oh, how he wanted a ride! But where was the centavo to pay for the ride?

"Maybe the owner of the merry-go-round will let me have a ride in trade for my bowl," he <u>thought</u>. "Maybe he will let me have three, six, or ten rides. I will take them one after another until my head swims and goes round and round like the ponies. Then I will forget all about the little green bird."

He thought of the bright eyes and the shining green feathers of the parrot which would never be his.

"In trade for this bowl, how many rides will you let me have?" he asked, walking up to the owner of the merry-go-round.

The man pushed his big hat far back on his head as he stood there thinking.

"Not any at all," the man said at last. "Not any at all."

Then he saw the disappointed look on Ramon's face.

"It's this way," he said. "I must have centavos for rides because I must pay centavos to the boys who push the merry-go-round. How could I pay them with a bowl? I would have to break it and give each one a piece. What good would a piece of bowl be to them? No, I must have centavos for rides."

"Maybe I could push the merry-go-round," said Ramon.

"Good," said the man. "I always need boys for pushing. Get under there and push the merry-go-round for two rides, and I will pay you one centavo. With that centavo, you can buy a ride."

"Then keep my bowl safe for me, and I will do it," said Ramon.

The merry-go-round came to a stop. When it started again, Ramon was under it, pushing and pushing, his feet flying in the soft dust.

Ramon pushed for two rides and earned one centavo. He <u>dropped</u> the centavo into the orange pottery bowl.

"I will push again and earn another centavo," he said to the owner.

Ramon pushed the rest of the morning. The hot afternoon came around, and most of the people in the market place went to sleep in the shade. Not the boys and girls! They went on riding. So Ramon went on pushing. He was very hot and very, very tired, but he went on working. He did not give up.

"I have never seen a boy who pushed so hard and so long," said the owner. "Rest a while, boy, and use one of your centavos to buy yourself a ride."

"Thank you, no," answered Ramon.

Every time he finished pushing two rides, the man gave him one centavo. Ramon dropped each centavo into the orange pottery bowl.

Poor Ramon never did take a ride.

Late in the afternoon, when everyone in the market place was <u>awake</u> again, he <u>crawled</u> out from under the platform, covered with dust from head to foot. He ran to get his bowl and <u>drop</u> in his last centavo. The pieces of money inside the bowl <u>jingled</u> merrily. Ramon counted them and grinned a happy grin.

"Twenty-one centavos!" he shouted. "It is more than enough. I go now, but I will be back again."

A Very Good Day, Indeed

Once more Ramon pushed his way through the crowd, looking for the weaver. At last he found him. He gave the weaver his orange-colored bowl with twenty centavos in it. In return, the weaver gave him a fine serape with beautiful bright-colored stripes.

Holding the folded serape high above his head, Ramon started for his father's stall. While still some distance away, he shouted, "Look, Papa! A new serape in place of a ragged one!"

He waved the serape before Sandino's astonished face. When Ramon told his story, Sandino gladly made the trade.

"You have done better business than I have today. Help yourself to my finest water jar," Sandino said, as he put his head through the hole in the new serape. By so doing, he turned the serape from a blanket into a fine overcoat.

The jar was almost as big as Ramon. It was hard work carrying it safely to the stall of the bird cages. Once he almost dropped it. He was glad when it was safely on the ground again.

"Here is a water jar made by Sandino, the potter," he said. "Now you can carry water from the river. In trade, I will take the cage with the little parrot."

"It's a trade," said the man.

He took down the cage and handed it to Ramon, who walked away with the cage in his hand.

Once more Ramon stood beside the merry-go-round. He gave the owner his last centavo.

"Now I would like to buy a ride," he said, with a happy grin.

"But I have no pushers. Everyone is getting ready to go home. Market day is about over!" exclaimed the man.

He was a kind man, a very kind man. When he looked at Ramon's unhappy face, he knew that there was just one thing for him to do. Just one!

"It is too bad that such a hard-working pusher as you should get no ride. I must push you myself."

There was hardly room for him under the platform, but somehow or other he crawled under and started to push.

Ramon, already up on a pony, was holding the cage in one hand while he waved his big hat high above his head with the other hand.

As the merry-go-round started to go
faster and faster, the parrot became more
and more excited.

"Hello! Good day! Hello! Good day!"
he screeched of his own accord, without
anyone to tell him. "Hello! Good day!"

"Yes, Mr. Parrot!" laughed Ramon,
as the pony went round and round. "It
has been a fine day. A good day! A
very good day, indeed!"

The sun was going down as Ramon, his mama and papa, and the little gray burro followed the steep road up the mountain. Ramon's father, in his new serape, walked beside the burro. Behind the burro walked Ramon's mother, and behind Ramon's mother walked Ramon, in his hand the cage with the little parrot inside.

Below, in the village, the <u>kindly</u> owner of the merry-go-round stopped to visit with the storyteller.

"I have a tale for you," he said. "A tale well <u>worth</u> the telling! <u>Add</u> it to the many others you tell so well. It is a story of Mexico. Its hero is a hard-working boy who dreamed of owning a little green bird, and worked until his dream came <u>true</u>."

Mountaintop

I would like to stand on a mountain
When its top is covered with snow.
Then I could look up
At the great blue sky
And down at the world below.
With the sun on my face
And the wind through my hair,
I could look all around me
And see EVERYWHERE.

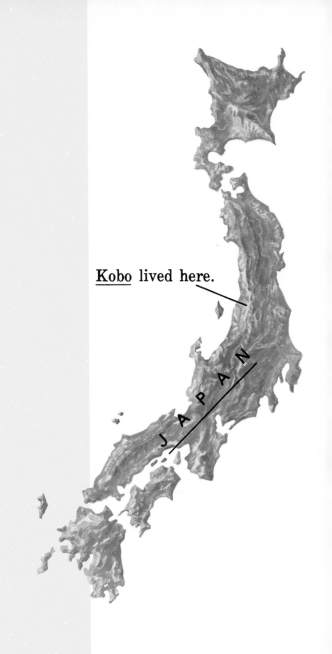

Kobo lived here.

JAPAN

117

Kobo and
the Wishing
Pictures

Helping Yourself with New Words
Picture Dictionary

brushes

clogs

flowers

horse

kimono
(kə mō′nə)

plum

pomegranate
(pom′gran′it)

tiger

Words You Can Get by Yourself

fish	clean	jingle	excite	lift
wish	mean	tingle	excitement	gift
		tingled		
giggle	well	may	young	find
wiggle	smell	pray	younger	mind
wiggling				
sled	in	how	sick	hat
slid	thin	bow	sickly	fat
boost	flop	weed	ear	high
roost	flopping	seed	dear	sigh
rooster				
all	trouble	feet	it	brave
tall	troublesome	sweet	itch	bravest
				bravely

118

cart	wrong	lip	tail	use
part	strong	ship	sail	using
	strongest			

boy	pet	will	white	arm
toy	petted	bill	whiteness	harm
				harmless

Two Words Make One Word

footsteps   everyday   fortunetelling

Let the Sentences Help You

1. A painter of pictures is an artist.

2. The sun is shining.
   David is his father's son.

3. I could hear the frogs croak.

4. There are two children in our family.

5. Answer me when I speak to you.

6. The sign said, "Danger — Drive Slow."   dangerous

7. Ann and David are both in my room at school.

8. The car started to roll down the hill.

9. My little sister is just a baby.   babies

10. I hung the picture on the wall.

Glossary

ar range (ə rānj′), to put in order. **ar rang′ing**

broad (brôd), wide; big across.

bus y (biz′ē), working. **bus′i est**

cus tom (kus′təm), the way things are always done.

cus tom er (kus′təm ər), one who buys.

eld er (el′dər), older.

em a (em′ə), a kind of picture to show one's wish.

Eng lish (ing′glish), the language spoken in the U.S.

e vil (ē′vl), wicked; bad.

fes ti val (fes′tə vl), a feast day or holiday.

for tune (fôr′chən), luck.

god dess (god′is), in Japan, a woman god.

hai (hī′ē), Japanese for "yes."

health (helth), feeling well. **health′y**

Hon or a ble (on′ər ə bl), a title given to someone who is great or good.

husk y (hus′kē), big; strong.

Ja pan (jə pan′), a country.

Jap a nese (jap′ə nēz′), belonging to Japan.

Ko bo (kō′bō), the name of a Japanese boy.

Mit su (mit′zü), the name of a Japanese girl.

plaque (plak), a piece of wood upon which a picture can be painted.

prob lem (prob′ləm), something to be worked out.

quick (kwik), fast. **quick′ly**

rice (rīs), a plant grown in warm countries; the seeds of this plant.

shrine (shrīn), a place where one may go to pray.

smooth (smüᴛʜ), flat; level.

sol emn (sol′əm), not wanting to laugh or smile.

squat (skwot), short; to sit on one's heels.

strange (strānj), queer; not often found.

stu pid (stü′pid), not making use of one's mind; not wise.

Tam a to mo (tăm ə tō′mō), a Japanese warrior.

treas ure (trezh′ər), something worth much; riches.

war ri or (wôr′ē ər), a soldier; one who fights in wars.

wres tler (res′lər), one who tries to throw or force another to the ground.

cap, fāce, cāre, fär; let, bē, wėre; it, īce; hot, ōpen, ôrder; voice, house; cut, pùt, tülip, ūse; th, thing; ᴛʜ, then; zh, garage; ə stands for *a* in about, *e* in angel, *i* in cabin, *o* in wagon, *u* in suppose

Wishing Day for Mitsu

Mitsu, the dark-eyed, dark-haired little Japanese girl, stood in the doorway of Miss Winters' schoolroom in Redwood City. Under one arm she carried a wooden plaque upon which was painted a most wonderful big brown squirrel. In her left hand was a book, on its cover a picture of a beautiful, snow-covered mountain.

Something important must have happened, something very important indeed. Why else should Mitsu look so happy and so excited?

"Do you know what this is?" she exclaimed, holding up the wooden plaque for everyone to see. "This is my Wishing Picture. It came with me from Japan. My grandfather, an <u>artist</u>, painted it for me. Today is not Wishing Day in Japan. In Japan, Wishing Day comes in the early spring. But in this country, today is MY Wishing Day because it is my birthday.

"Do you know what my Wishing Picture <u>means</u>?" Mitsu went on. "On the day I left Japan, I told Grandfather my one best wish. I wished that I could learn to talk <u>English</u> as fast and as well as a squirrel could chatter. This is why Grandfather painted me a squirrel. Now it is my birthday, and my wish came true.

"If you don't believe me, listen," Mitsu added. Her voice tingled with excitement. "See this book? It is my birthday gift from Japan. It tells about a Japanese festival day, the Festival of the Wishing Pictures. It is written in English, and in Japanese, too. It will make you wish that you had a grandfather to paint you a wishing picture."

Maybe you who are reading this book would like to see how Mitsu's book looked written in Japanese. But most of you could not read it if you did see it. So here, written in English, is the very same story that Mitsu found in her birthday gift from Japan.

Looking Forward to Wishing Day

Kobo slipped out of his wooden <u>clogs</u>. He dropped them onto the step outside the doorway of his house. Like everyone else in Japan, he must take off his clogs before going inside.

He sat for a minute in the warm sunshine and <u>wiggled</u> his toes. It was the first time this year that his toes had not tingled with the cold.

"Hai!" he cried out in excitement, as
he looked up at the first opening buds
on the plum tree beside the doorway.
"Spring is in the air. I can smell it.
And I can feel it, too. That means that
Wishing Day will soon be here."

Kobo smiled to himself, a pleased
smile that made his eyes sparkle and
his lips turn up at the corners.

Springtime in Japan means wishing time. Time to <u>pray</u> that the <u>rice</u> may grow well in the farmers' fields on the hillsides! Time, too, to wish for the one thing that you yourself want most in all the world!

Kobo sat there a little longer with the warm spring air on his smiling face. He wondered, "What is my one best wish going to be?"

That was something that would bear much thinking about.

Inside the house Kobo found his mother with Little Brother on her back. She, too, seemed to feel that spring was in the air. She was taking down the winter picture from the wall and putting in its place a springtime one.

In a green pottery bowl on the floor, Kobo's <u>younger</u> sister was <u>arranging</u> three plum branches with their first opening buds.

At the other side of the room, seated on the floor, was Kobo's father. He was an artist. The paints with which he was working made spots of bright color on the floor in front of him.

Springtime in Japan was the busiest time of year for an artist. Now with spring in the air, everyone would remember that the Festival of the Wishing Pictures would soon be here. On that day everyone would go to the shrine of the Rice Goddess, taking with him a picture of the thing he wished for most. He would pray to the Rice Goddess to make his wish come true. Each one would place his wishing picture on the wall of the shrine as a gift. Then the Rice Goddess would know what he wished for, and would not forget him.

"This year," thought Kobo, "I will bring a picture of my own. I will ask my father to paint it for me."

There were so many different wishes crowding around in Kobo's head! Which was the one for his wishing picture? What was the one best thing that he wanted most in all the world?

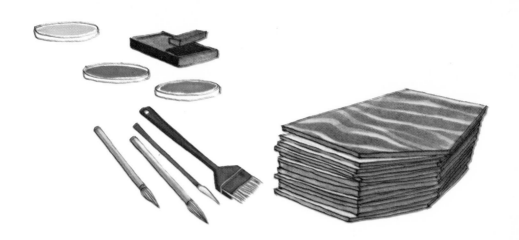

Footsteps at the Door

Just then Father looked up from his work.

"Come, Elder Son," he said. "Come and help me."

Kobo went over to where his father was working. On the floor were the wooden plaques on which the artist would paint the wishing pictures. With careful fingers, Father was feeling of each plaque to see that it was smooth enough for painting.

As Kobo counted the finished plaques, he arranged them in little piles on the floor.

"On one of the plaques," thought Kobo, "Father will paint my picture. But first I must know what my best wish is."

It was strange that he could not make up his mind. But not so strange after all! This was no everyday wish. It had to be the very best, the greatest thing that he could wish for. Maybe, if he listened carefully to what other people wanted in their wishing pictures, it would help him to make up his mind.

Already night was falling. Mother was cooking dinner. No one else would come today to ask the artist to paint a wishing picture. Kobo would have to wait until tomorrow. But NO! What was that? It was the sound of footsteps outside the door.

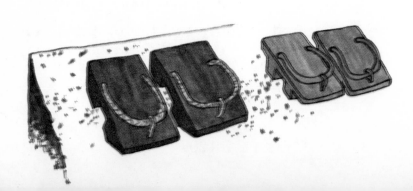

Mother went to the door and <u>slid</u> it
open.   Then into the house stepped
a <u>thin</u> little man.   Behind him stood a
very, very, very thin little boy.   Mother,
Father, Kobo, and Little Sister <u>bowed</u>
low before them.

"Honorable Artist," said the thin little man. "My son has been sick for a long, long time. He is still thin and sickly-looking, as you can see. My wish is for him to grow healthy and fat."

"Then," said Father, "I know just what I must paint for you."

He placed a wooden plaque on the floor in front of him. Slowly and carefully he started to paint. Everyone else in the room looked on without saying a word.

What Father painted was a <u>wrestler</u>, a champion wrestler, covered with great folds of fat.

"This will tell the goddess how you want your son to look," said Father.

All the time, Kobo was thinking to himself, "I would not like to be as big and fat as a wrestler. No, that wish is not for me."

After dinner, according to an old Japanese <u>custom</u>, Mother made up the beds on the floor. She covered Little Brother carefully from the cold. She patted Little Sister and touched Kobo with her warm fingers as she said good night. Still wondering about his wishing picture, Kobo fell asleep.

What Is My Wish to Be?

"Three more days to Wishing Day," Kobo thought to himself the next morning. "Today I must make up my mind."

While he was dressing, he thought about it some more. Then it was time for breakfast. Mother begged him to finish before the customers started to come. There would be many, many customers coming to see Father today.

Kobo was hardly through eating before he heard footsteps outside the door.

"Hai!" he called out. "Yes, I hear a customer coming. Maybe I will get an idea from him."

But the customer was a HER, not a HIM. A sad-looking, tired-looking woman! She bowed low before Father, her head almost touching the floor.

"Honorable Artist, please," she said to Father. "My son does not sleep at night. He stays awake and flops and crows all night long. So my wish for him is to become like a fine healthy <u>rooster</u>. A rooster sleeps all through the night and does no <u>flopping</u> or crowing until the sun comes up in the early morning."

"That is a wish well worth the wishing," said Father, as he started right in to paint the rooster.

Kobo looked around. Little Sister was grinning.

"Elder Brother," she said, "your eyes shut right after dinner each night. You can hardly wait to crawl into bed. It is easy to see that that wish is not for you."

The next customer to come in was a broad, squat man. He looked very cross. Behind him were six little girls. They giggled and put their hands over their faces. Then they giggled some more.

"Bad luck follows me everywhere I go," the man said. "My little girls are so stupid that they cannot learn to read or write. So please, Honorable Artist, paint me a picture of a mother frog showing her little frogs how to croak. Little frogs learn so quickly. Maybe the Rice Goddess can make my stupid girls learn to croak as quickly as little frogs. I do not mean to CROAK. I mean to read and write."

Kobo's father painted the picture, and the man seemed well pleased. Off he went with the six giggling girls.

Kobo, however, knew that he himself was good enough at learning. "So that wish," he thought, "is not for me."

There had been three customers already—the thin man last night, and the sad-looking woman and the cross man this morning. Not one had helped Kobo to make up his mind.

"Well," thought Kobo, "it is still early. Sooner or later someone has to come along with a wish that will give me an idea."

So he sat in the shade on the edge of the step and waited to see who would come next.

The next customer was a sad-eyed woman. She walked over to where Mother was feeding Little Brother. There were tears in her eyes as she said,

"Please, Honorable Artist, I have no children. I would like to have as many children as there are seeds in a pomegranate. So please paint me a red pomegranate with 1,000 seeds. Then the Rice Goddess will understand my wish."

"That wish!" Kobo said to Little Sister. "That is a wish you can have."

"NO, thank you," she answered. "When I grow up and have children of my own, two or three will be enough for me."

Once again Kobo went outside and stood under the plum tree to wait for more customers. He looked up the street to see who was coming.

"Mothers and girls!" he grunted. "Nothing but mothers and girls!"

And indeed Kobo was right. One mother after another came walking along, with their little girls dressed in beautiful bright kimonos.

"Oh, dear," sighed Kobo. "Not one of their wishes will be for me."

So it went on all day long.

The next morning Kobo waked with a start.

"Only two more days to Wishing Day," he said to himself. "Only today and tomorrow! I must make up my mind what my best wish is so that I can ask Father to paint it for me. And—oh—dear me! I haven't much time."

The first customer that day was a <u>tall</u>, <u>solemn</u>-looking man. He came through the doorway, pulling a little boy by the arm.

Once inside the house, the man said to Father, "Honorable Artist. I have the greatest of all <u>problems</u>. My boy is very bad and always in trouble. He kicks his sister and pulls her hair. He breaks everything to pieces just to be mean. He gets into my papers and mixes them all up. He throws his cap and coat into the mud. And the words he uses—oh, my! So I wish for him to see no <u>evil</u>, to <u>speak</u> no evil, and to hear no evil."

"Yes," said Father. "I understand."

見ざる　言わざる　聞かざる

And so Father painted the picture of a monkey. Not a <u>troublesome</u> one, but a very, very good monkey!

"This monkey does no wrong," explained Father. "See! It does nothing all day long but smell the <u>sweet flowers</u>."

The man thanked Father again and again. "This wish will put an end to all my problems. It is just the wish for my very, very bad boy."

But Kobo thought, "No indeed, thank you. I don't want to be as good as that monkey. Being good isn't for me."

By and by another customer came in with a troubled look on his face.

"I have a son," he said, "and my brother has a son. But our sons are so different." He sighed a big sigh. "So, Honorable Artist, I have come to bring you an order from my brother and to ask you to paint an ema picture, a wishing picture, for me, too.

"My brother's son, you see, is a very silly boy. He runs out into the street and pays no attention to cars or bicycles or carts or anything."

"He is indeed a dangerous actor," said Father. "So I will paint you a rabbit. Rabbits have quick ears to hear danger. That is what your brother's careless son should have."

"Not for me," thought Kobo. "I should not like to have long ears like a rabbit. I do hope that someone will soon wish a wish that is more for me."

It was a strange thing, but just then one of Kobo's ears started to <u>itch</u>.

"Oh, my!" exclaimed Kobo. "A right-ear itch means that something good is about to happen. A left-ear itch means that trouble is on the way."

For a second, Kobo couldn't make out which ear was itching. Then he found to his surprise that <u>both</u> ears were itching.

"So that tells me nothing," he thought.

He turned again to listen to the troubled-looking man.

"And now," the troubled-looking man was saying, as he sighed another big sigh, "I should like you to paint a wish that I have for my own son. He is afraid of everything. He screeches when a friendly dog wags its tail at him. He acts like a wild man when he has his hair cut. He jumps high into the air when he hears a bell jingle. And how he screeched when he cut his finger!"

"I see," said Father. "So I must paint you a picture of the bravest of all animals, the man-eating tiger. Then you can take it with you to the shrine of the Rice Goddess and pray that your son will be as brave as a tiger."

So Father painted a picture of a great man-eating tiger with black stripes.

"Hai!" thought Kobo. "That gives me an idea. To be brave is part of what I must wish for."

While Father added some finishing
touches to the picture, Kobo ran outside
and stood under the blossoming plum
tree. All the time, he was saying
over and over, "To be brave! To be
brave! That is a very good thing to
wish for."

At last he had an idea. Now that he
had an idea, he could take it to Father.
He would ask his father to paint a
picture to show his wish to be brave.

But look! Another man, a very husky
fellow, was on his way to the door.
Kobo followed him into the house.

The husky man didn't stop to explain why he wanted the picture he asked for. All he said was, "Please, Honorable Artist, paint me a picture of the great warrior, Tamatomo."

Kobo's face lighted up. Kobo knew that Tamatomo had been one of the greatest and strongest warriors in all Japan. Everyone in Japan had heard of him and was very proud of this great warrior. Maybe the husky man wanted his son to be brave and strong like Tamatomo. Or maybe he wanted the picture as a wish for himself.

Father started right in to paint the picture of Tamatomo while Kobo and the man looked on in astonishment. In bold colors on the wooden plaque, Father painted the strongest-looking warrior they had ever seen.

"To be strong! To be strong!" thought Kobo. "That is a good thing to wish."

Had Kobo made up his mind? He
had, almost. He would ask his father
to paint a picture that would show his
wish to be strong as well as brave.
He would ask his father, but when?

The Day before Wishing Day

It was late when Kobo crawled out of bed the next morning. The smell of plum blossoms came in through the open door. Father was already at work arranging his paints and brushes and wooden plaques on the floor. Little Sister, Mitsu, was talking to Mother.

"Only one more day until Wishing Day," she was saying, "and our family does not have one wishing picture to take to the shrine of the Rice Goddess."

Mother answered, "We hope that the goddess will remember us anyway. We will tell her that Father has been too busy, and we will whisper our wishes to her in our prayers."

A tear dropped from Mitsu's eye upon her bright-colored kimono. "If only someone in this family . . ." she started to say, but didn't finish. Kobo knew without asking who that someone was.

The first customer that day was a little fat man.

"Honorable Artist," he started in by saying.

The picture that he wanted was a treasure ship, sailing out over dangerous seas. Kobo knew what the meaning of that picture was supposed to be. According to an old tale told in Japan, a treasure ship would come sailing home when the sun went down. It would bring with it good luck for its owner, together with all the things he longed for most.

"Lucky! Lucky!" Kobo thought. "It is good to be lucky. Was there ever anyone who didn't want to be lucky?"

This was another good idea. He would ask his father to paint him an ema picture to show his wish to be lucky as well as strong and brave.

Morning went. Afternoon came. Still the sun of spring, high in the sky, did not warm Kobo. Father was too busy, and there had not been a minute for Kobo to tell him his wish. Soon today would be over, and Kobo would have no ema picture, no wishing picture, to take to the shrine tomorrow.

Kobo sat on the floor, crossed his legs, and wiggled his toes. Then all at once he knew what he must do. Why had he been so stupid? Now he had really made up his mind.

"With my own hands!" he whispered. "I must paint my own ema picture."

Kobo went over to the corner of the room where Father put the paints that he was not <u>using</u>. He helped himself to some colors, a brush, and a smooth wooden plaque.

All the time, he was thinking, "What is there that is brave and strong and lucky all at the same time?"

He knew something that would show the goddess his wish to be brave. One of those <u>roll</u>-over <u>toys</u> which looked like a little man! You could try again and again to tumble it over. The little man would <u>bravely</u> roll right up again.

He could think of something strong. A shark, swimming in the sea, would show his wish to be strong.

He could think of something lucky. A toy dog would bring good luck. Yes, indeed! A toy dog would bring him good luck, and good <u>health</u>, too. That is why toy dogs are given to newborn <u>babies</u> in Japan. But how could Kobo put all three wishes into one? That was the problem.

Kobo could feel something moving around inside his head—an idea wiggling. All at once that idea rolled from the back of his head to the front. At last Kobo knew, without any question, what he would paint.

He would paint a horse.

A horse was brave.

A horse was strong.

Since Kobo had been born in a year that is called "The Year of the Horse" in Japan, a horse would be a sign of good luck for him.

"Hai," thought Kobo. "Yes, a horse is brave and strong and lucky. All three in one! And other things, too!"

A horse could run like the wind.

A horse loved his master.

A horse could kick, too, if some evil one were not kind to him.

A horse was very wise. And a horse could be loved and petted by children.

Yes, it was a horse that he must paint to show the Rice Goddess his wish to be brave and strong and lucky.

Some people got their wishes. Some people didn't. As Kobo started to work, he wondered, "Will I get my wish?"

Quickly he fingered the plaque to see if it were smooth. He tried the brush. He tried the colors, one by one. Then, very carefully, he started to paint.

And there, at last, beautiful to look upon, was his horse.

Wishing Day at Last

The morning of the Wishing Day Festival came at last. There was a feeling of excitement in the air. Everyone was dressed in his very best. Mother and Mitsu put on their most beautiful kimonos. <u>Baby</u> Brother was fastened safely to Mother's back. Only Father had a strange, faraway look on his face. Something was wrong. What could it be?

"I know," sighed Mother, as she turned to speak to him. "You are an artist, and this is the busiest time of year for you. You have not had time to paint an ema picture for your own family."

Baby Brother seemed to know that Father was unhappy, and his lips turned down at the corners.

But Kobo was not feeling sad. With a happy laugh, he ran to get his wishing picture, and he gave it to Father.

Father's troubled look turned to a pleased smile.

"I am very happy," he said, "for if Elder Son is brave and strong and has good luck come to him, then we, who love him so much, will have a part in his good luck. Good <u>fortune</u> will come to all of us."

There were proud tears in Kobo's eyes. It was now more important than ever that the Rice Goddess should make his wish come true.

At last the family was all ready to leave for the shrine. Father, Mother, and the children joined the crowd of people going in at the gate through which everyone must go on his way to the shrine. According to the Japanese custom, everyone left his wooden clogs on the doorstep outside the shrine.

On the walls inside the shrine, people <u>hung</u> their ema, their gifts to the goddess. Then each one stopped to pray, his head bowed low.

The thin man hung his wrestler.

The tired-looking woman hung her healthy-looking rooster.

The broad, squat man hung his croaking frog.

158

The sad-eyed woman hung her pomegranate with its many seeds.

The tall, solemn-looking man hung his monkey, smelling the sweet flowers.

The troubled-looking man hung both his brother's rabbit and his own tiger.

The husky man hung his picture of Tamatomo, the bravest and strongest warrior in all Japan.

The fat man hung his treasure ship.

And—Kobo hung his horse.

As he whispered a prayer to the goddess, Kobo hoped for a sign to show that he would get his wish, but no sign came.

The Fortunetelling Bird

As Kobo and the rest of the family left the shrine, they came upon a little man with a fortunetelling bird.

"Please, Father," Kobo asked. "May I have the bird tell my fortune?"

"Hai! Hai!" Father answered. "Yes, of course, Elder Son."

Kobo gave some money to the man, and the bird man opened the cage.

Out hopped the bird, hop, hop, hop across the table to the place where a little toy shrine was standing. It looked like the shrine Kobo had just left.

Ting-a-ling rang the doorbell when the bird touched it with its bill. The door of the shrine slid open. The bird bowed its head over the doorway. It pushed with its bill into a pile of folded papers. Push, push, push through the papers— pushing, pulling.

Kobo tingled with excitement.

"He is looking for my fortune," Kobo thought to himself. "And now he has it."

The little bird had a folded piece of paper in its bill and was bringing it to Kobo.

"Thank you! Thank you!" said Kobo.

Just then Kobo's eyes lighted upon a tree beside the road. Onto the tree's branches were fastened many pieces of white paper. Those papers, Kobo knew, were the bad fortunes which people wanted to leave behind them.

"Oh, dear me," thought Kobo. "Not everyone gets the fortune he wants."

Then came the sign. His right ear started to itch. Kobo sighed a sigh that came from his toes up. He was so excited that he could hardly open the folded paper.

"What will it say?" he wondered.

Then he knew. On the paper, written in Japanese, were the words:

あなたの望は実現するでしよう

In English, the Japanese words mean:
YOUR WISH
WILL COME TRUE

俳句

Spring is in the air.
Buds on the plum tree today,
Tomorrow blossoms.

Rain, please fall softly.
Summer sun, please shine brightly.
Make my rice grow tall.

Leaves slip softly down.
In an orange-colored world
Summer turns to fall.

In night's dark stillness
Snowflakes robe the ground below
In winter's whiteness.

俳句

Gray and white pigeons
Sat on my roof in the sun,
Talking together.

One wild brown rabbit
Eating my flowers and grass.
Why must I feed you?

Pink and white tulips
Make long ribbons of color
By my garden wall.

A <u>harmless</u> green snake
Crawls up on the garden wall
To sleep in the sun.

164

Good Luck Duck

SCOTLAND

Timothy
lived in
this valley.

165

Helping Yourself with New Words
Picture Dictionary

Ferris wheel

hoops

mouth

oil can

shoe

monkey wrench

Words You Can Get by Yourself

tingle	tell	let	mad	see	pipe
tingling	till	lot	lad	wee	piper
rain	hard	but	sing		merry
train	hardest	bit	sang		berry
					blueberry
noise	earring	hair	fine		most
noisy	ring	fair	line		mostly
noisier					
speak	face	hand	prize		jingle
speaker	race	handful	size		jingling
	racing				
went	again	thank	red		dry
tent	against	tank	rid		dried

well	hope	sing	tied	busy
<u>yell</u>	hopeful	string	<u>untied</u>	<u>busily</u>
	<u>hopefully</u>	<u>shoestring</u>		

hoop	lock	six	sea but	long
<u>stoop</u>	<u>cock</u>	<u>fix</u>	pea nut	<u>song</u>
			<u>peanut</u>	

down	am	excited	found	loud
<u>drown</u>	slam	<u>excitedly</u>	<u>pound</u>	<u>loudest</u>
	<u>slammed</u>			

high	lock	care	right	would not
<u>highest</u>	<u>rock</u>	<u>dare</u>	<u>might</u>	<u>wouldn't</u>

Two Words Make One Word

<u>understood</u>   <u>streetcar</u>   <u>beeline</u>   <u>loudmouth</u>   <u>outshouted</u>

<u>wildfire</u>   <u>otherwise</u>   <u>runaway</u>   <u>nohow</u>

Let the Sentences Help You

1. Stars <u>twinkle</u> in the sky at night.   twinkled
   twinkling

2. Someone who walks with you is your <u>companion</u>.

3. Button your coat up around your <u>neck</u>.

4. If I miss the bus, what <u>shall</u> I do?

5. You need an <u>engine</u> to pull a train.

167

Glossary

bon ny (bon'ē), fine.

burr (bèr), a way of talking in which one trills the letter *r*.

con tin ue (kən tin'ū), to keep on. **con tin'ued**

deaf (def), not able to hear.

dis gust (dis gust'), a feeling of disliking very much. **dis gust'ed**

e ven (ē'vən). *Not even* means not as one would expect.

grab (grab), to catch hold of. **grabbed**

hor ri fy (hôr'ə fī), to shock. **hor'ri fied**

hun ger (hung'gər), the feeling one has when one needs food. **hun'gry**

hur ry (hèr'ē), to move quickly. **hur'ried**

jum bo (jum'bō), very big.

knock (nok), to hit. **knocked**

lev er (lev'ər), a bar used to lift something at one end by pushing down at the other end.

nib ble (nib'l), to eat by taking little bites. **nib'bling**

qui et (kwī'ət), still. **qui'et ly**

Scot land (skot'lənd), the name of a country.

shil ling (shil'ing), a piece of money worth about 14 cents.

squawk (skwôk), a loud, unpleasing sound. **squawked squawk'ing**

stone deaf (stōn'def'), entirely deaf.

stretch (strech), to pull out and make longer. **stretched**

swamp (swomp), wet, soft ground.

taste (tāst), to take a small bite of.

tast y (tās'tē), good or pleasing to eat.

Tim o thy (tim'ə thē), a boy's name.

toss (tôs), to throw lightly.

val ley (val'ē), a low place between hills.

cap, fāce, cāre, fär; let, bē, wėre; it, īce; hot, ōpen, ôrder; voice, house; cut, pùt, tülip, ūse; th, thing; ᴛʜ, then; zh, garage; ə stands for *a* in about, *e* in angel, *i* in cabin, *o* in wagon, *u* in suppose

Grandmother's Story

Six girls at once tried to crowd through the doorway of Miss Winters' schoolroom in Redwood City. Ann Parks was one of them. When you are tingling with excitement, you sometimes forget about pushing and pulling.

"Wait till you hear this," they started to say. At a sign from Miss Winters, the rest of the girls stopped talking and let Ann continue.

"I'm sorry," Ann went on. "We didn't mean to act this way. But we have lots to tell you. My grandmother from Scotland is coming to visit me. And what do you think, Miss Winters! She wants to come to school to see our map. She wants to see my name card and all the rest of the name cards, too. I told her all about the map in my letter. Today I had a letter from her to say she was coming.

"Will it be all right if she comes to school someday?" Ann continued.

"All right? Nothing could be better," was Miss Winters' answer, and all the boys and girls agreed.

"She is little and lots of fun," Ann went on. "And she talks with a burr. Just wait till you hear her. Daddy likes to joke. Once he told her that her voice needed some oil."

So it happened that a week or two later a not-too-old grandmother with a twinkle in her eye stood in front of the map in Miss Winters' schoolroom. She listened to the chitter-chatter going on around her, and she looked at all the cards.

At first Grandmother's burr made her hard to understand, but just at first. When Mark grinned at Windy and then covered his face with his hand to stop the giggles, Grandmother understood.

Her blue eyes twinkled more than ever as she said, "Come to Scotland, my lads. Give the lads over there a chance to giggle at you when they hear YOU talk. They will do it, too."

When there was not another thing to see on the map, down Grandmother sat. Everyone gathered around her.

"Well, now," she started in by saying. "I have just the tale for you. It's about a wee lad I used to know in Scotland. A wee lad with a bonny white duck for a pet!"

Everyone sat listening as Grandmother started her story.

Quiet Valley

It was a quiet valley. It was a friendly house. I mean the little white house where Timothy lived with his mother and father. I mean the quiet valley three miles down Piper's Road, just after you pass Alexander's Wood. That valley!

The streetcar did not get there. The bus did not go that far. The trains rolled miles away in a bigger valley of their own. But Timothy's house was in a quiet valley—a round bowl of a valley.

The crows calling all day in Alexander's Wood could not be heard there. They were too far away. The trains rolling all night in the bigger valley could not be heard. They were too far off. At night rabbits played in the quiet valley. But rabbits can play the <u>hardest</u> games and still not make a <u>bit</u> of noise. And the birds in Timothy's valley <u>sang</u> only in the morning and a little at night.

Timothy loved his quiet valley. But sometimes the valley was so quiet it made him wish that some good fortune would bring him a pet to be with him all day long—a pet and a <u>companion</u>.

Someone to play with him in the valley! Someone to walk with him along the edge of the <u>blueberry</u> <u>swamp</u>! Someone to run with him down Piper's Road to listen to the <u>noisy</u> crows in Alexander's Wood! A dog, maybe!

"Dad," Timothy would say, "may I have a dog for a pet?"

But a dog would chase the rabbits and drive them from the valley. Maybe a cat!

"Mother," Timothy would tease, "may I have a cat?"

But a cat would catch the birds and drive them from the valley. Then it would no longer be a friendly valley with the birds singing in the morning and a little at night.

A pet that would not chase rabbits? A harmless one that would not catch birds? What kind of pet could that be? Timothy did not want a pet like that.

Since there was no pet to play with him, once a year Timothy wanted noise. Once a year the quiet in the valley became too much for Timothy. It became too much for his mother and father, too. Once a year they all wanted noise— horses running, people shouting, bells ringing, wheels turning, lights twinkling, and so on and still more.

So once a year they all went to the fair, for what is noisier than a fair?

There was only one way for Timothy and his mother and father to get to the fair. That was to walk three miles down Piper's Road to the end of the streetcar line. They would catch the streetcar at this end of the line and ride it ten miles to the other end of the line. The fair was at the other end of town. It took time.

They all liked to do about the same things at the fair every year.

Timothy's father went <u>mostly</u> to visit with his old friends and to hear the <u>speaker</u> of the day. Timothy's mother went mostly to see the horses <u>race</u>. But Timothy went to ride the <u>Ferris</u> wheel. He never got tired of the Ferris wheel. Sometimes he had 30 rides, one after another. This year it was going to be the same way.

Inside the Gate

The streetcar got them to the fair at about ten in the morning. Just before getting off the car, Timothy's mother gave him a <u>handful</u> of <u>shillings</u>. He put that lady-<u>size</u> handful of shillings into his left-hand sweater pocket. Just after getting off, Timothy's father said, "Here!" He, too, gave Timothy a handful of shillings. Timothy put that man-size handful of shillings into his right-hand pocket. Then, <u>jingling</u> his treasure as he ran, he made a <u>beeline</u> for the Ferris wheel.

"Wait for us at the Ferris wheel," called his father.

Timothy shook his head to say yes and waved good-by.

Just as Timothy passed the first tent inside the gate, he happened to look up. Then he stopped, staring with his mouth open. The Ferris wheel was not running. There it stood in the distance, cold and dark against the sky. It did not move. It did not twinkle. The lights were out.

Timothy was looking so hard at the dark Ferris wheel that he did not hear the little man in front of the first tent shouting at him.

Ring a Duck

Again the little man shouted.

"RING A DUCK—WIN A DUCK.
RING A DUCK—TAKE HOME A DUCK."

This time Timothy heard him. The man had hung some wooden <u>hoops</u> on his arm. He had more in his hand.

"Here, boy," the little man said. "You want to win a duck. Here! Ten hoops for a shilling."

Timothy shook his head.

"I don't want any," he said.

"Of course you do," said the man, as he tried to push some hoops into Timothy's hand. "They are to throw around the <u>necks</u> of the ducks I keep in a <u>tank</u> in my tent. See that tall woman? That is what she is doing. If one of her hoops goes around the neck of any duck, that duck is hers—to take home. Ten hoops for a shilling!"

Just then the tall, thin woman turned around and saw Timothy.

"Please, boy," she called, "will you ring a duck for me? I just can't ring a duck, and this is my last hoop."

What was Timothy to do? The woman stood waiting. He had to help her.

Inside the tent there was a tank, and in the tank were some ducks. Ten black ducks and one white duck were swimming in the water. Around and around sailed the black ducks.

The woman handed Timothy her last hoop.

Timothy did not think he could ring one of the black ducks. Those ducks were swimming so fast that he could not hope to toss a hoop around one of their necks. But the white duck was different. He just sat in the middle of the tank with his eyes shut. Anyone could have mistaken him for a toy duck if it had not been that he was quacking loudly. The tent rang with his quacking.

Timothy bit his lip hard and tossed the hoop. Down it went over the white duck's yellow bill. Down it went over his white neck. But the white duck never stopped his quacking. He did not even open his eyes.

"I did it! I did it!" Timothy shouted to the little man outside.

The little man came running, but the tall, thin woman was just disgusted.

"Not that one!" she told Timothy.
"Who wants a <u>loudmouth</u> duck like that?
I could have done that myself."

"But you didn't tell me," said Timothy.
"How was I to know?"

"Well, anyone would know that," she
said, more disgusted than ever.

The little man slipped the hoop off
the white duck's neck. He handed the
duck to Timothy.

Timothy tried his best to give the duck to the tall woman.

"I should say not," she said. "Do you think I want to walk around this fair with a loudmouth duck like that?"

"But he belongs to you," said Timothy.

"Well, then YOU keep him," said the woman. She brushed Timothy aside and ran out of the tent.

"Don't leave him here. I don't want him," said the little man. "For weeks I've been trying to get rid of that duck. People win him, but they always bring him back. No one wants a loudmouth duck like that to carry around the fair. People slip him back into the tank when I'm not looking. But not you! You won't put him back. I've seen to that. I've taken steps."

The man shouted right in Timothy's face. The duck shouted back at him. The one outshouted the other.

What Shall I Do Now?

All at once Timothy found himself pushed out into the street with the quacking duck under his arm. Everyone, even the babies, stared at him.

"Boy, make that loudmouth duck stop quacking!" shouted one fat woman.

A farmer stopped Timothy, and Timothy tried hard to give him the duck.

"No, I don't want him," the farmer said. "I just wanted to see how one duck could make so much noise. Why, he is noisier than 50 frogs in a dried-up pond. You had better ship him back to where he came from." And the farmer walked on.

Timothy had no idea what to do now. No one wanted him around. He had to go somewhere. He went on walking until he came to the merry-go-round. He did not think that he could ride with a quacking duck, but he could try.

The lady at the ticket window sold him two tickets without saying a word. Timothy <u>hurried</u> over to the merry-go-round. The duck under his arm quacked louder than ever when he heard the music.

"No ducks!" <u>yelled</u> the man who ran the merry-go-round.

Merry-Go-Rot

PLEASE BUY YOUR TICKET

"But I have a ticket for him," said Timothy <u>hopefully</u>.

"Can't help that! No ducks!" The man took Timothy's two tickets and gave him back his money.

Timothy stopped at the pony rides. He did not even try to buy a ticket. The man would not so much as let him stand at the gate for one good look at the ponies.

"Get away from here with that <u>squawking</u> thing!" he yelled at Timothy. "<u>Hurry</u> up about it, too."

Timothy had no idea what to do now. He couldn't ride the merry-go-round. He couldn't even look at the ponies. The Ferris wheel was not running. But come now. Maybe he did know what to do. If he got rid of the duck, his troubles would be over.

He put the duck down right in the middle of all the passing people. Then he tried to hurry away. He couldn't.

Something was pulling at Timothy's shoestring. When Timothy looked down, he saw that it was the duck. One of Timothy's shoestrings had come untied. The duck had it in his mouth.

As Timothy looked down, the duck did a funny thing. He started to nibble the shoestring. While he nibbled, he whispered busily to the shoestring. The little busy whispers sounded happy.

Timothy stooped to tie his shoestring. He stooped way over.

The minute Timothy stooped, he was <u>knocked</u> down by someone passing in the crowd. All around him were moving feet and legs. He tried to get up. He almost got up, but he was knocked down again. He <u>grabbed</u> for the duck and tried again. At last he made it.

"Did you see that?" he asked the duck. "They almost walked right over us."

Timothy knew now how all those moving feet and legs must have looked to a little duck.

"Never you mind," he whispered. "I did not know it was like that down there. I won't put you down again to be stepped on."

The little duck listened. It cocked its bright head. Then it stood right up in Timothy's hands. It stretched its neck up and ran a nibbling bill all over Timothy's face. It stretched its bill around to Timothy's ear. Then very softly, very busily, very happily it whispered happy little whispers right into Timothy's ear.

"Why, you . . . why, you," said Timothy. "You whisper to me when I whisper. Why, you are a smart duck."

Timothy couldn't get rid of that duck now—not any more. That funny little whispering duck! He liked him.

What Do You Know about That?

Since he could not and would not get rid of the duck, Timothy had to think up a plan. He thought hard about it.

First, go to the Ferris wheel! Maybe it would start running—but if not—find a quiet spot—stay there with the duck—wait for his mother and father to come. That was all there was to Timothy's plan.

The Ferris wheel at the edge of the fairgrounds was a quiet spot. No one was anywhere around. There was just the Ferris Man trying to <u>fix</u> the Ferris wheel <u>engine</u>. There was just a <u>Peanut</u> Man resting on an upturned box with his basket of peanuts beside him.

This was a good place for the duck. He cocked his bright little head. He stopped quacking. He seemed to listen to the quiet. Then he went sound asleep right under Timothy's arm.

The Ferris Man looked up from his
work when he saw Timothy and the duck.

"No one rides my Ferris wheel," he
said. "It's always breaking down."

"No one buys my peanuts," said the
Peanut Man. "It's my squawking voice.
My voice is always breaking down."

"No one wants me around," said
Timothy. "It's my duck. He is so noisy.
So may I stay here? He will be quiet
here because this is a quiet place."

"You may stay," said the Ferris Man,
"but it won't be much fun for you."

Timothy sat down beside the Peanut Man. The duck was still sound asleep.

"It's my squawking voice," the Peanut Man said again. "When people hear my voice, they don't want any peanuts."

"It's not your voice. It's your no-good song," said the Ferris Man, as he went on working. "You need a new song."

"Maybe we could make up a new song," said Timothy. "That would be something to do. That would be fun."

"Let me see now," the Ferris Man said, thinking and working at the same time. "How about this for a start: Peanuts, peanuts! Buy my peanuts."

"Great big tasty, jumbo peanuts," added Timothy for the next line.

The Ferris Man went right on: "Taste them, try them. Don't forget to buy them. How does that sound?"

"Tasty, tasty, TASTY peanuts," added Timothy to bring the song to an end.

"Sing it all! Quick! Before we forget it!" the Peanut Man said to Timothy.

Timothy sang very softly in order not to wake up the duck.

"Peanuts, peanuts!
Buy my peanuts.
Great big tasty, jumbo peanuts.
Taste them, try them.
Don't forget to buy them.
Tasty, tasty, TASTY peanuts."

"There is your song. Sing it that way, and people will buy all kinds of peanuts," laughed the Ferris Man.

"I'll try," the Peanut Man said.

Just then the little duck waked up.

The Peanut Man started to sing in his loud, squawking voice. The duck started quacking along with him. The Peanut Man sang louder to <u>drown</u> out the duck. The duck quacked louder to drown out the Peanut Man. The louder the noise, the more trouble Timothy had in holding on to the duck. The noise was too much for the Ferris Man.

"Stop it! Stop it!" he yelled.

He lifted his monkey <u>wrench</u> high above his head and <u>slammed</u> it down on the Ferris wheel engine. He slammed it down again and again and again. The noise was driving him wild.

All at once the Peanut Man let out a screech.

"The Ferris wheel!" he cried, yelling and pointing at the same time.

The Ferris wheel had started. The lights twinkled. The slamming of the monkey wrench had started the engine.

Timothy put the duck down on the
upturned box and danced around in his
excitement.   But the Ferris Man just
stood where he was, with his hand on
the lever, too surprised to move.

"It's going," he said, over and over
again. "Why, it's going.   Now what do
you know about that?"

I'll Take a Chance

The Peanut Man sang no longer. Timothy stopped dancing.

"Now may I ride the Ferris wheel?" Timothy shouted. "Now may I?"

He took out his father's man-size handful of shillings. He dropped them all into the Ferris Man's big hand.

"They are for me to ride the Ferris wheel—oh, lots of times!" he cried excitedly.

"If you want to take a chance," said the Ferris Man. "Remember what I told you. It's always breaking down. Suppose it stopped while you were way on top, lad. How would we get you down?"

Timothy was willing to take a chance.

"You will let my duck ride, too, won't you?" he begged.

The Ferris Man pulled the big lever, and the wheel stopped. Then he looked at the duck on the upturned box.

"Well, now, let me see," said the Ferris Man with a big grin. "Shall we say two rides for a shilling for a duck? Is that about right?"

"Oh, fine, fine!" shouted Timothy.

He did not wait for the Ferris Man to say another word. He dropped his lady-size handful of shillings on top of the ones in the Ferris Man's big hand. He hurried to get the duck and climbed into a seat with the duck beside him.

"Ready! I'm ready!" he shouted.

The Ferris Man pushed the big lever. The Ferris wheel started. Up went Timothy and the duck. The duck stopped his quacking. He liked the ride. He liked being up. He liked it far above the noisy fair. He whispered excited little whispers to Timothy. He thought that he was flying.

Up went Timothy and the duck. Around and around and around again!

Then it happened. It happened just as the Ferris Man had said it would. It happened just as Timothy and the duck were at the very top. The lights twinkled out. The Ferris wheel stopped.

Timothy looked down from his high seat. There stood the Peanut Man, looking up with his mouth open. There was the Ferris Man, pushing on the big lever. Pushing and pulling!

Minutes went by. Timothy sat looking down at the crowded streets of the fair. He was not afraid. Up there it was fun for him and for the little duck. It was exciting. He even started to sing the Peanut Man's song very, very softly.

Down below the Ferris Man had stopped pushing and pulling on the lever. That was getting him nowhere. The Ferris wheel did not start. Once more he lifted his monkey wrench high above his head and slammed it down on the engine. He pounded away at this and then at that.

It was fun for the duck until that pounding started. The duck couldn't stand that noise. He stretched his neck far down over the edge of the seat and quacked his loudest.

The Ferris Man couldn't stand that. "Make that duck keep still!" he yelled at Timothy. "Make him shut his mouth. Do you want to stay up there forever?"

Excitement in the Air

People walking along the streets heard a duck squawking high up in the air. They stopped and looked up. There, dark against the sky, they saw a Ferris wheel with a boy and a duck on the highest seat. The news flew like wildfire. Everyone came running. The crowd shouted things at Timothy. The duck shouted back. The yelling of the crowd could not drown out his quacking.

"Make that duck shut up!" the Ferris Man yelled up at Timothy. "Otherwise I can't work, and if I can't work, you may stay up there forever."

"Maybe he is hungry!" shouted someone in the crowd. "Maybe if you feed him, he will stop squawking. Quick! Peanut Man! Some peanuts!"

Before many seconds went by, broken bags and peanuts were raining down on the crowd. But not one bag could fly high enough for Timothy to catch it.

The Ferris Man grabbed the last bag in the Peanut Man's basket. He opened the bag and put a rock inside.

"Stand back! Stand back!" he yelled, as he tied the bag. Then he let fly.

Up went the bag of peanuts, higher and higher, right toward Timothy.

Timothy did his best. He stretched out his arms as far as he dared. He almost made it. But—he missed.

Timothy missed because just at that
second the lights twinkled on. The
Ferris wheel had started again.

"They're coming down! They're coming
down!" everyone shouted.

Down came Timothy and the quacking
duck—but up they went again. Around
and around and around again! Now that
the Ferris wheel had started, it would
not stop.

This news, too, flew all over the fair: "BOY AND DUCK ON A RUN-AWAY FERRIS WHEEL. THEY CAN'T STOP IT NOHOW."

The crowd was big before, but it was ten times bigger now. With the crowd, came Timothy's mother and father.

Timothy's father took one horrified look. Then he pushed through the crowd and did not stop until he was right by the side of the Ferris Man.

"Stop that thing and get my boy down from there!" he yelled.

"My dear man, I can't!" the Ferris Man shouted back at him. "Don't you think I'm trying as hard as I can?"

Timothy's father gave a push that almost knocked the Ferris Man over. Then he pulled the lever with all his might. He pushed the lever with all his might. He pushed and pulled till the lever almost broke off in his hands.

Then the Ferris wheel stopped—just when Timothy and the duck were almost on the ground. His father lifted Timothy off, duck and all.

"Stupid!" shouted Timothy's father at the Ferris Man. "Nothing is wrong with your wheel. All it needs is oil."

"Oil!" exclaimed the astonished Ferris Man.

He ran to get a can of oil. He put oil on the lever and some on the engine, too. He pushed the lever. The Ferris wheel started. He pulled the lever, and the Ferris wheel stopped.

"Why, it works!" he shouted. "Now what do you know about that?"

Timothy's father had not seen the duck when he lifted Timothy from the seat of the Ferris wheel. He was too excited. Now, for the first time, he looked at the duck in Timothy's arms.

"How did you—where did you—what in the world are you doing with that squawking thing?" he wanted to know.

When he heard about the tank— when he heard how Timothy had tried to ring a duck for a lady by tossing a hoop around its neck—when he heard that the man would not take the duck back, Timothy's father was disgusted.

"So he pushed this duck off on you. He wouldn't take him back. He has taken steps, has he? Well, I'll take steps, too. Big steps! Wait till I get my hands on him. Give me that duck."

Timothy's father grabbed the duck and pushed through the crowd with big steps. The poor duck was squawking loudly.

Timothy's father was mad, but not the Peanut Man. The Peanut Man was happy. He had sold the last of his tasty, jumbo peanuts. That duck was a good luck duck for him.

The Ferris Man was happy, too. Now that the Ferris wheel was really fixed, everyone wanted a ride.

"Come back any time. Have all the rides you want—for nothing," he said to Timothy. "That good luck duck, too."

"And all the peanuts you can eat," added the Peanut Man. "All for nothing!"

Another Quiet Valley

Timothy did not pay a bit of attention to what the two men were saying. His mother had him by the hand and would not let go. But he was pulling her along with him as he tried to run.

"Hurry, PLEASE!" begged Timothy. "My dad has gone to get rid of my duck. I've got to stop him. I've just got to!"

By the time Timothy and his mother got to the duck tent, the little man was running as hard as he could around the tent with Timothy's father racing after him. They were shouting at each other. The air rang with their shouts.

"Stop it!" called Timothy's mother to his dad. "Don't you see that a crowd is gathering? What are you thinking about?"

Just as Timothy's dad put out his hand to <u>grab</u> the little man, the man stooped and got away. He came to a stop beside Timothy's mother.

"Please," he begged. "Won't you take the little duck home with you? He can't stand noise. He hates noise. He isn't used to noise, and he never will be.

"He hates noise because he always lived in a quiet valley," the man went on, looking down at Timothy.

Timothy's face showed his surprise.

"Well, now! This is strange," said Timothy's mother. "Tell us some more."

"In that quiet valley stood a little white house," the man continued. "In it lived a little old lady. The little duck liked to sleep on her doorstep."

A QUIET VALLEY! A LITTLE WHITE HOUSE! Timothy could not believe what he was hearing.

"The little old lady was deaf—stone deaf. She thought she was talking out loud, but she always talked in whispers. Because she talked in whispers, her little duck talked in whispers, too."

"Yes!" exclaimed Timothy. "That is just what he did to me. He whispered right in my ear."

"He was the old lady's pet and companion," the little man said next. "He talked to her by her shoestring. She always left one shoestring untied. The duck would nibble her shoestring to call her attention."

"Yes, yes, that is what he did to me!" shouted Timothy. "He nibbled my shoestring, but I did not know why."

"When she could feel him nibbling, she would lift him in her arms. Then he would whisper right in her ear."

"Why, that is what he did to me. Right in my ear," said Timothy.

"Sometimes the little old lady took walks in the quiet valley with the duck. She would walk along the edge of the swamp so that the little duck could swim and catch frogs and little fishes."

That was almost too much for Timothy.

"Mother! Dad!" he shouted. "She had a quiet valley! And a white house! And even a swamp!"

"Why—do you have a quiet valley?" asked the little man excitedly.

"Oh, yes, and a white house," said Timothy. "Not too far from a blueberry swamp."

"Do the birds sing in the morning and a little at night?" asked the man.

"Why, yes, they do," said Timothy.

"Do rabbits play in the moonlight?"

"They play the hardest games and never make a bit of noise," Timothy said.

"Then that is where the duck belongs," said the little man. "The little old lady became too old to live out in the country down a road where no bus came and no streetcar ran. She had to move to the city, and a city is no place for a duck. It is far too noisy."

"But you," the man continued. "You have a quiet valley, a little white house, and a doorstep. You must take him home. I told the little old lady that I would find a good home for him. But I live only from one fair to the next, and what is noisier than a fair?"

"Dad," begged Timothy. "I've got to take him home."

"Of course you do," said the man.

"Of course you do," said Timothy's mother.

"Guess you do," said Timothy's dad with a big grin, as he handed the duck to Timothy.

Good Luck Duck

In the schoolroom in Redwood City, everything was as still as could be. By this time everyone had forgotten that Grandmother had come from Scotland and talked with a burr. Everyone was too busy listening to her story.

"I wish I could tell you of all the trouble Timothy had getting his duck home on a streetcar," said Grandmother, "but my story is too long now. This I can tell you. By the time Timothy and his mother and father had come to the end of the line, the duck's quacking had come to an end—almost.

"He did not quack at the trains rolling miles away in a bigger valley of their own. He could not hear them. He quacked a little at the noisy crows in Alexander's Wood. He whispered one or two sleepy quacks at the croaking frogs in the blueberry swamp.

"But the bonny wee duck was fast asleep by the time they came to the white house in the valley," Grandmother continued. "At the back doorstep Timothy put him down. The duck opened his eyes. He stood up in surprise. He cocked his bright head and listened to the quiet in the valley. He found Timothy's shoestring and nibbled it a little. Then he fell asleep with the shoestring in his bill.

"Timothy carefully slipped his foot out of his <u>shoe</u> and stepped <u>quietly</u> into the house. He shut the door softly and then opened it again.

"'Good luck, duck,'" Timothy whispered. "'Good luck in your new home.'"

"It was quiet in the valley. The birds had already finished their good-night songs. The moon came up to shine down on the doorstep. Rabbits slipped out to play their games. But by the white doorstep, Timothy's little good luck duck was fast asleep in the moonlight."

Just Me

Ferris wheel, I have my eye on you.
All by myself I will ride on you.
Remember to stop
When I'm way up on top.

What fun it will be
To look down and see
Fire engines racing
Out from the town.
Out from the town
To get me down.

Just ME.

The Peddler of Ballaghadereen

Miss Winters'
great-grandmother
lived here.

IRELAND

Helping Yourself with New Words
Picture Dictionary

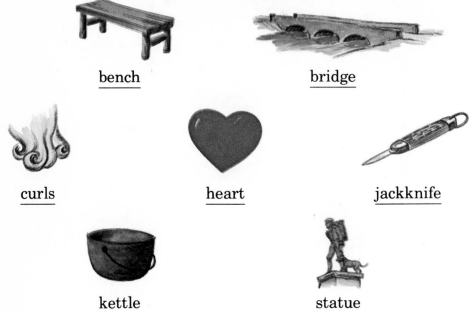

bench

bridge

curls

heart

jackknife

kettle

statue

Words You Can Get by Yourself

all	city	ice	hung	plan	mouth
small	cities	twice	hang	plant	mouthful

merry	pull	pipe	lock	sweet
cherry	full	ripe	flock	sweeter
cherries		ripen		sweetly

dark	back	strap	follow	jackknife
darken	pack	strapped	hollow	knife

make	sad	like	easy	pass
shake	sadly	likely	easily	lass
shaking			ease	lassie

cage	beg	head	tell	broad
age	begging	bread	teller	abroad
end	sat	might	fair	forget
spend	sit	mighty	fairy	forgetting
			fairies	
feels	light	pass	cross	rub
heels	lighter	passer	crosses	rubbed
hungry	bird	four	tie	big
hungrier	third	fourth	die	dig
hunger				digging
old	wake	grab	cover	nest
gold	waking	grabbing	uncover	chest
workman	good	live	glad	face
workmanship	goodness	living	gladden	facing

Two Words Make One Word

sidecars   blackbirds   thereabouts   roadside

wherever   livelong   whatever

Let the Sentences Help You

1. Those skates belong to Bill.
   These skates belong to me.

2. Just then it began to rain.

3. Cut the apple in two and give me half.

4. There is no water in the bowl.

   The bowl is <u>empty</u>.

5. I have eaten nothing all day.

   My <u>stomach</u> is empty.

Glossary

Bal lag ha der een (ba la ha dėr ēn'), a village.

crea ture (krē'chər), any living person or animal.

cu ri os i ty (kyu̇r'ē os'ə tē), a wish to find out something.

Dub lin (dub'lən), a city in Ireland.

inn (in), a place to eat and spend the night.

Ire land (īr'lənd), a country.

land lord (land'lôrd'), the keeper of an inn.

latch (lach), a catch to keep a door shut without using a key.

Lif fey (lif'ē), a river in Ireland.

man ners (man'ərz), ways of acting, good or bad.

nod (nod), to bend the head a little and then raise it again. **nod'ded**

ped dler (ped'lər), one who travels around, selling things.

sat is fy (sat'is fī), to give one enough of what he wants.
     sat'is fied   sat'is fy ing

six pence (siks'pəns), a piece of money worth about 7 pennies.

thieve (thēv), to steal. **thiev'ing**

trav el (trav'l), to go from one place to another.
     trav'el er   trav'eled   trav'el ing

trin ket (tring'kit), a ring or other bit of jewelry, not worth much.

turf (tėrf), dry grass and roots, used for burning.

wea ry (wir'ē), tired.

cap, fāce, cãre, fär; let, bē, wėre; it, īce; hot, ōpen, ôrder; voice, house; cut, pu̇t, tülip, ūse; th, thing; ᴛʜ, then; zh, garage; ə stands for *a* in about, *e* in angel, *i* in cabin, *o* in wagon, *u* in suppose

Pictures and Places

"Look, Mark! They're here! No more waiting around now!"

David Mays stood in the doorway, took one quick look around the schoolroom, and then ran over to look at the many <u>small</u> pictures which were hanging beside the world map on the wall.

In the next minute or two, questions were popping here, there, and everywhere, as other boys and girls crowded around him. There was some friendly pushing and pulling as everyone tried for a place up in front where he could see better.

"Did you really take these pictures, Miss Winters? Boy, they're keen! Is Ireland as green as people say it is? When your great-grandmother lived there, did she live in a stone cottage like this one? Is this really a turf fire burning? Sidecars! Is that what you call these two-wheeled donkey carts?"

On and on went the questions. Miss Winters, with some last-minute work to finish, said "Yes, yes," over and over and over again as if there were only one right answer to every question. However, she ended up with these words: "In your seats now, all of you. Work comes before play. Not another word out of you about those pictures until the right time comes."

A great big disappointed "AW" went up all around the room. But no one tried to make Miss Winters give in. Everyone knew better than that.

So it was the end of the afternoon, work over for the day, when Miss Winters pointed to her name card on the world map and <u>began</u> her story.

"This you must remember," she began by saying. "The Ireland I saw when I was over there this summer was very much like our own country. Big <u>cities</u> and towns, highways and cars, and people and <u>travelers</u> everywhere.

"But off the well-<u>traveled</u> highways, in some almost forgotten places, there are still small villages with white cottages like the ones you see in my pictures. I suppose it was in a cottage like one of these that my great-grand-mother was born. The village she lived in is in a lovely valley, ringed round with green hills and the blue mountains. I wouldn't be surprised if you could shut your eyes and see that village in your mind's eye."

Minutes went by. Then, holding up a picture for all to see, Miss Winters continued.

"One night I sat in this very cottage. On a <u>bench</u> before the fire sat an old, old man with merry blue eyes and music in his voice. Night came softly down, and in the stillness we could hear the sea birds call. While the turf fire burned and the <u>kettle</u> sang, this is the old, old story of Ireland which he told to me. 'Is it true?' you may ask. Maybe not, but I wish it were. Listen, and maybe my story will make you feel that way, too."

Cabin at the Crossroads

More years ago than you can tell me and <u>twice</u> as many as I can tell you, there lived a peddler in Ballaghadereen. He lived at the crossroads by himself in a bit of a cabin with one room to it. It was so small that a man could stand in the middle of the floor, and, without taking a step, he could lift the <u>latch</u> on the front door, he could lift the latch on the back door, and he could hang the kettle over the turf. That is how small it was.

Outside the cabin the peddler had a bit of a garden. In it he <u>planted</u> the vegetables that would grow well and make a tasty <u>mouthful</u> for his table. In the middle of the garden there was a <u>cherry</u> tree—as brave and fine a tree as you would find anywhere in Ireland. Every spring it flowered, the white blossoms covering it like new-fallen snow.

But every year, soon after the garden was planted, the wee brown rabbits would come hurrying from the green wood. They would nibble-nibble here, and nibble-nibble there, until there was hardly a thing left to grow into a full-sized vegetable that a man dared cook to put upon his table. And every summer, as the cherries started to ripen, the blackbirds came in flocks to eat the cherries as fast as they began to turn red.

The rest of the people who lived thereabouts were horrified. They nodded their heads and said, "It's a poor silly man you are, Master Peddler. You let the wild creatures thieve from you without lifting a hand to stop them."

The peddler would always nod his head back at them and laugh and answer, "Now, then, it's not thieving they are at all. They pay well for what they take. Look you! On my cherry tree the blackbirds sing sweeter than they sing on any other cherry tree in Ballaghadereen. And the brown rabbits are my good companions when night comes round to darken the sky above my head."

With a Pack on His Back

When it was market day in the country round about, or there was a fair maybe, the peddler would be off at ring-of-day, his pack strapped on his back, one foot ahead of the other, carrying him along the road. And when he came to the next town, he would rest on the grass or on some rock by the roadside and open his pack. Then, making a hollow of his two hands, he would call:

"Come buy a ring—come buy a ball—
Come buy a ribbon, blue or yellow."

In no time at all there would be a crowding of children about him, looking his pack over for what they might be wanting. And like as not, some wee lad would hold up a jackknife and ask, "How much for this, Master Peddler?"

And the peddler would answer, "Three shillings."

The lad would put back the knife, shaking his head sadly.

"I haven't a shilling to my name," he would answer, "and I'm not likely ever to have one."

Then the peddler would pull the lad over to him and whisper in his ear, "Take the knife, lad. It will rest far more easily in your pocket than in my pack."

Then, like as not, some lass would hold up a blue ribbon to her yellow curls and ask, "Master Peddler, how much must I pay you for this?"

And the peddler would answer, "One shilling sixpence!"

The lass would put the ribbon back, the smile gone from her face, and she turning away.

Then the peddler would catch up the ribbon again and tie it himself about her curls and laugh and say, "It looks far more beautiful there than ever it looked in my pack. Take it, lass, and may good fortune follow you wherever you go."

So it would go—a doll to this one and a top to that. There were days when the peddler took in little more than a shilling or two. But after those days, he would sing his way homeward.

The wise ones, seeing him passing by, would wag their fingers at him and say, "Is it deaf to our words you are, Master Peddler? Not a sixpence have you put by for your old <u>age</u>. You will end your days like the blackbirds, <u>begging</u> for <u>bread</u> at our back doors. Even the dogs know that you will give them the <u>half</u> of the bread you have in your pocket."

And their words were true. Every hungry dog, up and down the land, knew the Peddler of Ballaghadereen. Never did he follow a road without one of them wagging his tail beside him.

A Teller of Tales

There were days when the peddler went abroad without his pack—when there was no market day and no fair. Those days he liked to spend with the children, who would have followed him around like the dogs, had their mothers let them.

On those days he would sit himself down on some doorstep, and when a crowd of children had gathered, he would tell them tales—old tales of Ireland—tales of her mighty heroes and of the good little people, the fairies.

The Peddler of Ballaghadereen knew all the old tales, and he knew how to tell them, the way the children would never be <u>forgetting</u> one of them, but carry them in their <u>hearts</u> until they were old.

Whenever he finished a tale, he would say, like as not, laughing and pulling the curls of some wee lass, "Mind well your <u>manners</u> both at home and abroad. You never can be telling what hero you may be passing on the road, or who may come knocking at your door. Every hero who lived in Ireland was once a lad or <u>lassie</u> like yourselves. You never can be telling. One of you today may be a hero tomorrow. So keep a kind word for everyone."

Many a grown-up, stopping to listen to his words, would <u>shake</u> his head and think to himself, "The poor, poor man! He is as silly as the blackbirds."

Spring followed winter in Ireland, and summer followed fast upon the <u>heels</u> of both. Winter came again, and the peddler was growing old. Day by day his pack was growing <u>lighter</u> and lighter, until <u>passers</u>-by could hear the <u>trinkets</u> jingle inside, for his pack was almost <u>empty</u>.

Then the wise ones nodded their heads and said to one another, "Like as not, his pockets are as empty as his pack. He cannot go on pounding the roads forever. Time will come, with winter at hand, when he will be at our back doors begging bread, along with the blackbirds."

The Peddler's Dream

The time did come, as the wise ones said it would, when the peddler's pack was empty, when the peddler had nothing in his pockets and little or nothing to eat in his bit of a cabin. That night the peddler went hungry to bed.

Now it is more than likely that hungry men will dream, and the peddler of Ballaghadereen had a strange dream that night.

He dreamed that there came the sound of knocking in the middle of the night. Then the latch on the front door lifted, the door opened without a sound, and inside the cabin stepped a tall and kindly man. Standing in the doorway, the good man pointed his finger and said in a voice tuned as low as a summer wind over the grasses.

"Peddler, Peddler of Ballaghadereen, take the road to Dublin town. When you come to the bridge which crosses the Liffey, you will hear what you are supposed to hear."

In the morning the peddler waked and remembered the dream. He <u>rubbed</u> his <u>stomach</u> and found it empty. He tried his legs and found that they would hardly hold him up. So he said to himself, "An empty stomach and legs like my own are poor <u>traveling</u> companions. I'll stay where I am."

That night the peddler went <u>hungrier</u> to bed, and again came the dream. There came the knocking on the door, the lifting of the latch. The door opened, and the good man stood there, pointing the road and saying.

"Peddler, Peddler of Ballaghadereen, take the road that leads to Dublin town. When you get to the bridge which crosses the Liffey, you will hear the words you are supposed to hear."

The next day was the same as the first, only the peddler was hungrier than ever, and he stayed where he was.

Dublin Town

When the peddler waked after the third night and the third coming of the dream, he dressed and strapped his pack on his back as was his custom in the old days. Then he took the road to Dublin town.

For three long and weary days he traveled with hardly a bit of bread to break his fast. On the fourth day he came to the city. Early in the day he found the bridge that crossed the river Liffey.

All the livelong day he stood there,
resting first on one weary leg and then
the other, moving his pack around on
his back to ease the feel of it. He
stared at the faces of all who passed.
A great crowd of people crossed the
bridge one way, and a great crowd of
people crossed the bridge the other way,
but no one stopped to speak to him.

At the end of the day he said to
himself, "I'll find me a hollow place by
some roadside. Then, like an old dog,
I'll sit myself down in it and die."

Slowly he moved off the bridge. As he passed by the Head Inn of Dublin, the door opened, and out came the landlord. The peddler looked up in astonishment as the landlord crossed the road and hurried after him.

"Hold a minute, Master Peddler!" cried the landlord. "All day I have had my eye on you. All day I have seen you standing on the bridge like an old crow with wings too weary to fly. Of all the people crossing the bridge one way, and of all the people crossing it the other way, no one had a word for you. My curiosity is very great. What brings you here?"

Seeing by his face how hungry and weary the peddler was, the landlord pointed toward the inn.

"Come," he said. "In return for satisfying my curiosity, you shall have bread and whatever else you wish, to satisfy your empty stomach."

So the peddler rested his weary legs by the turf fire in the kitchen. Soon he was eating as he had not eaten in many days. At last he was satisfied, and again the landlord asked the question, "Peddler, what brings you here?"

"For three nights running, I had a dream," the peddler began, but the landlord waited to hear no more. Throwing back his head, he laughed. How he laughed, rocking on his feet, shaking from head to foot.

"So it's a dream you had—a dream!" he said, when he could stop his laughing. "I could tell by the looks of you that you were the kind of man to have dreams, to listen to them, and to believe in them, too. Rags on your back, hunger in your face, and age upon you, and not a sixpence in your pocket. If it's a dream that brings you here, turn your footsteps homeward before you fall by the wayside."

The peddler got to his feet, lifted his pack, and made for the door. He had one foot over the doorstep when the landlord took hold of his arm with a strong hand.

"Hold, Master Peddler," the landlord said. "I, too, had a dream, three nights running. I dreamed that there came a knocking on this very door, and the latch lifted. Standing in the doorway, as you are standing now, was a tall man in a long white robe. He pointed with one finger to the road which you followed on coming into town, and he said.

"'Landlord, Landlord of the Head Inn, take that road to Ballaghadereen. When you come to the crossroads, you will find a wee cabin, and beside the cabin a wee garden, and in the middle of the garden a cherry tree. <u>Dig</u> deep under the tree, and you will find <u>gold</u>— much gold.'"

Once again, throwing back his head, the landlord laughed loudly.

"Ballaghadereen!" he cried. "I've never heard of the place. Gold under a cherry tree! Who ever heard of gold under a cherry tree? There is only one dream that I hear, <u>waking</u> or sleeping, and it's the dream of gold, much gold, in my own pocket. That is the dream to believe in. That is the only gold you can count on. Listen to this, Master Peddler." And the landlord put his hand into his pocket and jingled the money inside in the peddler's ear.

Gold under the Cherry Tree

Back to Ballaghadereen went the peddler, one foot ahead of the other, carrying him along. How he got there on his poor weary legs, I cannot be telling you. Once at home again in his bit of a cabin, he eased the pack from his back. Then grabbing the shovel which stood by the bench at the door, he started to dig under the cherry tree. He went on digging until his shovel came upon something hard and smooth.

It took the peddler time to <u>uncover</u> the treasure. When he did, he found it to be an old sea <u>chest</u> of strange and wonderful <u>workmanship</u>. When he broke the lock, rusty with age, he found the chest full of gold pieces, twice as many as anyone in Ireland has ever seen before or since.

I cannot tell you the half of the <u>goodness</u> the peddler put into the spending of that gold. But these things I do know.

The peddler still went on living in his bit of a cabin, so small that a man, without taking a step, could stand in the middle of the floor and lift the latch on the front door, lift the latch on the back door, and hang the kettle over the fire.

Each spring he planted his bit of a garden, and the wee brown rabbits and the other wild creatures from the wood came thieving, until there was hardly a full-sized vegetable left to put upon his table. The blackbirds came in flocks to eat the ripening cherries and, in return, they sang more sweetly here than they did in any other cherry tree in Ballaghadereen.

On sunny days the peddler traveled the roads with a pack on his back and a dog at his heels. And many a trinket from his pack gladdened the hearts of the lads and lassies round about.

"Remember your manners always," he would say with a nod of his head, as he handed a ball, a top, or a jackknife to some wee lad.

"The fairies are listening," he would say to some wee lass, as he put a ring on her finger or a ribbon on her curls. "So have a kind word for everyone."

At long last the peddler died, and the people of Ballaghadereen, remembering his goodness, had a <u>statue</u> made of him and placed it <u>facing</u> the crossroads. And there he stands to this day with a pack on his back and a dog at his heels.

Fairies

Lass
With the red-gold hair,
Have you ever seen the fairies?

———————

Once
In a meadow green,
I have seen
Fairies dancing in a fairy ring.
Once
On a summer night,
In soft moonlight,
I heard the sound of little bells.
It was the fairies singing.

———————

Lass
With the red-gold hair,
Do you believe in fairies?

———————

Yes,
In my dreams.

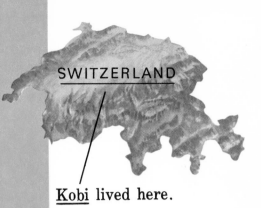

SWITZERLAND

Kobi lived here.

251

Kobi,
the Herdboy

Helping Yourself with New Words
Picture Dictionary

bucket

geraniums

handkerchief

spoon

umbrella

vest

Words You Can Get by Yourself

her	hat	an	sit	wake	eat
herd	hit	pan	sitting	waken	beat
herder		pants		wakened	beaten
how	joking	white	dress	or	big
cow	jokingly	Whitie	press	short	pig
lively	lock	T-shirt	feather	grass	back
live	stock	shirt	leather	brass	crack
alive	stocking				
catch	well	dream	sail	hope	trip
snatch	sell	dreamless	trail	rope	tripped
rest	catch	leave	tomorrow	fine	wave
restless	patch	leaving	morrow	mine	waving
	patches		borrow		

small	eye	broad	strong	count
smaller	eying	broadly	stronger	counter

Two Words Make One Word

herdboy	halfway	farmhouse	summertime
grandson	crosspiece	cowbells	goatherders

Let the Sentences Help You

1. I heard a noise.
   I saw a herd of cows.

2. My ring is not gold. It is silver.

3. The rug covers the floor.

4. A cow gives milk.
   One who milks a cow well is a good milker.

5. On each hand, I have a thumb and four fingers.

6. He tore a hole in his shirt this morning.

7. Cows are sometimes called cattle.

8. When did you pay that bill?
   I paid it last week.

9. My dress is too big around the waist.

10. A man who fixes shoes is a cobbler.

Glossary

alp (alp), a high mountain.

Alps (alps), the name of the mountains in Switzerland.

ark (ärk), the boat God told Noah to build.

ar rive (ə rīv′), to come to a place.
                          ar rived′

blond (blond), light-colored.

brac es (brā′siz), suspenders.

cal lus (kal′əs), a hardened place on the skin. **cal′lus es**

dis ap pear (dis′ə pir′), to go out of sight. **dis′ap peared′**

ex cept (ek sept′), but.

ex plode (eks plōd′), to break out with a loud noise. **ex plod′ed**

fa vor ite (fā′vər it), liked better than others.

flash (flash). To do something like a flash is to do it quickly.

franc (frangk), a coin used in Switzerland.

Franz (fräntz), a man's name.

Gurt (kürt), the name of a cow.

in sist (in sist′), to say over and over that something is so. **in sist′ed**

Ja cob (yä′kəb), a man's name.

jan i tor (jan′ə tər), one who takes care of a building.

Ko bi (kō′bē), a boy's name.

moun tain eer (mount′n ir′), one who lives in the mountains.

No ah (nō′ə), the man in the Bible whom God told to build the ark.

pa rade (pə rād′), to march or walk with others in a long line.
                          pa rad′ed

pelt (pelt), to beat or hit.
              pelt′ed   pelt′ing

pro tect (prə tekt′), to keep from harm. **pro tect′ing**

Sepp (sep), a boy's name.

Switz er land (swit′sər lənd), the name of a country.

---

cap, fāce, cãre, fär; let, bē, wėre; it, īce; hot, ōpen, ôrder; voice, house;
cut, pùt, tülip, ūse; th, thing; ᴛʜ, then; zh, garage; ə stands for *a* in about,
e in angel, *i* in cabin, *o* in wagon, *u* in suppose

254

Curiosity

Bonny Shepherd and Mr. Franz, the janitor, had a secret. Anyone with a bit of imagination could tell that. For three days now this is the way the talk had been going on between them.

First Day

"Did you find it, Mr. Franz?"

"Dear me, I forgot to look."

Second Day

"Did you remember this time?"

"I remembered all right, but when I was through work, I was tired enough to die. Too weary to do anything else."

Third Day

"Did you have time last night?"

"Yes, but I couldn't find it. It must be in that old chest up under the roof. I'll look there tonight."

Everyone else in Miss Winters' schoolroom was full of curiosity. But no one could satisfy his curiosity. Even Ann, Bonny's best friend, couldn't do that. Some people guessed one thing, some another, but no one <u>hit</u> upon the right answer.

This is how it all began. One night Bonny was staying after school so that Miss Winters could help her with some work which she had missed when she was out sick. Mr. Franz came in just then to clean the windows. He stopped long enough to take a look at the world map as he was passing by. At that minute, Bonny and Miss Winters happened to look up. They saw what he was doing.

"By the way, Mr. Franz," said Miss Winters. "Why not put your name card up there? You came from another country, didn't you?"

"Can't be done," grinned Mr. Franz. "The country I came from has a card on it already. The card is bigger than the country—almost."

"It is!" cried Bonny, forgetting all about work and hurrying over to see.

"Why . . . why . . . why, Mr. Franz," she was saying the next minute. "That is my card, and that is where my ancestors came from. Mom and Dad have never even been there. Did you live in Switzerland? Did you really?"

"I did for twenty years," said Mr. Franz. "If I am not mistaken, I still have something at home which belonged to me when I was a boy over there."

Now, if you are any good at all, you have the secret figured out—halfway.

On the fourth afternoon, when Miss Winters' room came in from the playground, Mr. Franz was standing in the schoolroom doorway.

"Here you are, young lady," he said, handing a big suit box to Bonny.

Once inside the door, Bonny was too excited to untie the string. Mr. Franz had to help her. Then what did she hold up? Some goatskin <u>pants</u> and a bright red <u>vest</u> with flowers and <u>silver</u> buttons all down the front!

"It is a herdboy's suit, and it belonged to Mr. Franz when he was a herdboy in Switzerland!" exclaimed Bonny, her voice tingling with excitement.

Another minute, and everyone was out of his seat, crowding round to see.

"Could we try it on? Could we?" every boy started in teasing, every boy but Windy Chase.

"Something is missing! Am I right? Isn't there, Mr. Franz?" he <u>exploded</u>.

"Missing?" said Mr. Franz, feeling under the paper in the box. "Why, boy, you are right. It's the . . . ."

"DON'T TELL—DON'T!" exploded Windy. "Do you know how I knew? I have a book at home about Switzerland. The boy in the story couldn't be a herdboy until he earned money to buy his—. Boy, I almost let the cat out of the bag. I'll bring that book to school tomorrow."

"And I'll take another look tonight," said Mr. Franz. "A herdboy could never be a herdboy without his—."

What was missing from that suit? I hope you know a good way to find out.

A Good Milker

"Kobi, Kobi, if you don't get dressed right away, there won't be any breakfast left."

Mother's voice rang through the old farmhouse. In his room up under the roof, Kobi was sitting on the edge of the bed, wiggling his toes in the goatskin rug. The good smells from the kitchen had already wakened him. Now he pulled on his warm pants and slipped an old sweater over his blond curls.

Kobi's house was very old. For over 200 winters the snow had <u>pelted</u> against it. For over 200 summers the rain and the sun had <u>beaten</u> against it. And in all those years the snow, the rain, and the sun had turned its wooden walls to a deep, dark brown.

Outside the windows the pots of red <u>geraniums</u>, that had lived all winter inside the house, were a sign that winter was over. No more snow! No more cold winds! Spring was already here.

Up the hillside behind the house stretched the deep, dark woods. It was so big that the children could walk through it for miles and never get out of its deep shadows. Above the treetops, one could see the great, high mountains which were always white with snow except in the summertime.

Kobi put on his big outdoor shoes, for he must milk the cow before he could eat any breakfast. Down to the kitchen he went, two steps at a time. If Mother had been stone deaf, she still could have heard him coming.

Father was through milking, but Kobi could hear Grandfather singing in the barn. Grandfather had his own cow, and Kobi had his. Grandfather's cow was stubborn and did not give down her milk easily. Grandfather sang the same song to her each milking time. He said that she milked more easily then.

Kobi took a wooden milk bucket from the kitchen table and opened the door into the barn. The barn was like another room fastened onto the kitchen. Grandfather stopped singing.

"Slowpoke," he called jokingly. "I'm almost through milking. Gurt thought that you were never coming."

Gurt, Kobi's cow, turned her head and her big eyes to look at Kobi. Kobi began to milk her. He was slow, but he was a good milker. When he finished milking a cow, that cow had no more milk to give. It was the same way with Whitie, his goat. Father said so.

Kobi had helped with the milking ever since he was 9 years old. He had a hard callus on his thumb. The callus came from pressing his thumb against his four fingers as he milked. Grandfather and Father had calluses on their thumbs, too, but their calluses were bigger and harder than Kobi's. They had milked cows for many years.

The milk hit against the side of the bucket, singing a friendly tune. Time passed. When the bucket was half full, Gurt was milked. Grandfather and Kobi let the hungry animals out of the barn to eat the grass, which was still not very long. Summer seemed to be a long time in coming this year.

The two milkers carried their buckets into the kitchen. They joined the rest of the family at the breakfast table.

Breakfast was no sooner over than a loud knock came on the outside door.

Uncle Jacob

Kobi ran to open the door. In walked
Uncle Jacob, Kobi's favorite uncle, with
a big bundle under his arm.

Uncle Jacob was broad and short,
young and brown. His hair curled all
over his head just like Kobi's, but his
curls were black. Kobi had been named
after his uncle: Kobi, short for Jacob.
Uncle Jacob said that Kobi belonged half
to him and half to his mother and father.

"Smells good around here!" laughed Uncle Jacob, wiggling his nose like a rabbit.

"Come in, Jacob," called Mother, when she heard his voice. "There is still some breakfast left for you."

"Well, before I make up my mind," said Uncle Jacob, "I have a question to ask Kobi."

He pulled an old bench up to the table and pulled Kobi down beside him. In a low voice, so that no one else could hear, he whispered in Kobi's ear.

"I need a boy to milk cows and feed pigs and cut wood. I've been thinking of all the boys I know, and I think you are just the boy. Would you like to come up into the Alps this summer and herd cows? Can you milk?"

Kobi was so excited and surprised that he could not speak. He stood there like a statue, holding out his thumb.

Uncle Jacob looked that thumb over carefully. He saw how big the callus had grown. Then he whispered again, "I can see by that callus that you have milked a lot of cows."

Now at last Kobi had come alive.

"When do we go?" he shouted.

"First," said Uncle Jacob in a voice that everyone could hear, "here is a present for you, my boy."

He handed the big bundle to Kobi.

Kobi tore off the newspapers from around the bundle and pulled out—.

"Some goatskin pants! A herdboy's
vest! This is a herder's suit. Is it for
me, Uncle Jacob?" yelled Kobi.

Before he was through talking, he
had already put on the vest, and it looked
as if it had been made for him. Now
he stood there, holding the yellow pants
up against him.

"Your little sister can't use it, since
she is a girl. Your mother would look
funny in it. It is too small for me now.
So it must be for you, Kobi," said Uncle
Jacob, with a merry laugh.

"Maybe your mother has some long white stockings for you," Uncle Jacob continued. "Grandfather must have an old white shirt for his grandson. But the braces, Kobi! The black leather braces with little figures of cows on the crosspiece—those you must earn for yourself. I don't know how, but you must find a way."

Until Uncle Jacob left for home, Kobi followed him around, staring at him with his eyes shining and his toes dancing. There was only one thought in Kobi's head. How was he to earn money for those black leather braces? How was he to do that?

Angels round My Bed

That night when Kobi was fast asleep in his little wooden bed, he had a dream. He dreamed that he was herding cows on a mountain meadow. In the middle of the meadow was a great rock that had fallen down from the mountain many years before. It was almost as high as Kobi's house.

On top of the rock sat two angels with wings of gold. In their hands were some black leather braces. On the crosspiece of the braces were three cows made of brass. Those were the braces Kobi must have.

"Climb up onto this rock, Kobi," called the angels, "and we will give you the braces that go with your yellow pants and your red vest."

Kobi began to dig his toes into the cracks of the rock. He climbed up and up and up until he was right on top.

Every time Kobi touched the braces, the angels <u>snatched</u> them away from him. At last they flew upward into the night sky. As he tried to catch hold of their feet, they <u>disappeared</u> over the mountain-tops.

Kobi waked with a start. He peeped out from under the covers. The room was black and very, very cold. He could hardly believe that he had been dreaming. He could hardly believe that the angels were not real.

Kobi sat up in bed in the cold and dark. He tried to think how he could ever earn money to buy those braces. If only it were late summer, he might help the men in the fields. It would take 16 <u>francs</u> to buy those braces. So Uncle Jacob had told him.

For some time Kobi sat there, shaking with the cold and thinking and thinking, but he could think of no way to earn money. At last he stretched his legs out under the covers and tried his best to go to sleep. But every time when he was almost asleep, up popped those angels to wake him again.

If only he could <u>sell</u> something. He had a fine knife. The landlord of the village inn had given it to him. But Grandfather said that it was worth only 8 francs when it was new, and 8 francs were not 16 francs.

At last Kobi had an idea.

He could sell his goat, Whitie. Whitie was over 5 years old, and that is very old for a goat. Only the other day Kobi had heard Father tell Grandfather that that goat would be eating her head off in another year. Eating more than she was worth!

Kobi could sell Whitie at the <u>cattle</u> fair in the village. There were cattle fairs in the village every two weeks. What was it that Kobi had read on the sign in the inn? Yes, he remembered:

CATTLE FAIR AND SPRING FAIR, MAY 25

May 25? Why, that was just next Saturday. Kobi ducked farther down into the darkness under the covers. Now he could rest. No more angels could tease HIM. In a minute or two he fell into a <u>dreamless</u> sleep.

The Cattle Fair

The big, round sun was just coming up on May 25 as Kobi started down the mountain <u>trail</u> which joined the road leading into the village. In the pack on his back was his noontime lunch. His goat, Whitie, a <u>rope</u> around her neck, <u>tripped</u> along behind him.

The road, when he came to it, was crowded with farmers driving their unwilling cattle to market. The cows were a soft gray color like Kobi's cow, Gurt, and like most of the cattle one sees in Switzerland.

Boys on bicycles passed by. In the baskets on their backs were baby pigs and goats. Everyone was going to the village to sell something: a horse, a cow, a pig, or a goat.

When Kobi <u>arrived</u> at the market place, he could hardly make his way through the noisy crowd of men and animals. At last he found the goat market and tied Whitie safely to a wooden post. Many other goats were there, waiting for buyers: black, brown, white goats— young goats, fat goats, old goats.

Kobi knew by the way the people were dressed that they came from far back in the mountains. This morning they were having a grand time, walking around and cracking jokes at every animal they saw. They tried to make the owners of the goats think that their animals were not worth anything. Whitie came in for her turn, too.

One old mountaineer stopped in front of Whitie and began to feel of her all over. He looked into her mouth to see how old she was. He shook his head and laughed so loudly that a crowd started to gather around him.

"I'll give twenty-five francs for her," he said. "How about it, boy?"

"Not enough!" exploded Kobi. "Father said that she was worth 50 francs."

"If you ever get 50 francs for that old goat, we will get black snow," laughed the farmer, as he walked away.

"Black snow," thought Kobi. He had heard Grandfather say that many times. "That farmer must mean that I will never get 50 francs, for snow is never black."

Every time Kobi asked 50 francs for Whitie, the mountain people laughed. Not one of them thought that Whitie was worth much of anything, even if Kobi did <u>insist</u> that she was a good milker.

By this time Kobi was tired. He stood
first on one foot and then on the other.
He was hungry. So he opened his
lunch bag and took out the two apples
he found there. Once he had eaten
them, he began to feel better.

Next to the goat market were stalls
where people were selling boxes of
growing flowers, homemade rugs, and
other things, even some oranges from
Italy. Above the noises of the market
place Kobi could hear the deep sound
of the cowbells which were being sold
in the bell market.

Goatherders came, and goatherders
went. They passed by the post where
Whitie was tied, but no one stopped.

Kobi had just about made up his mind
to take Whitie home. Just then he
heard a shout. He looked up, and there
stood Sepp, his very best friend. Kobi
could hardly believe his eyes.

A Friend in Need

"Are you selling Whitie today? Are you really?" asked Sepp.

"I thought I was," answered Kobi, "but no one seems to want her."

Then he told Sepp about the herdboy suit and the braces he must earn.

"I came down to sell two baby pigs for Father," said Sepp. "Sold them right away! Father told me to take out one franc for my trouble."

Sepp jingled the money in his pocket.

"Why can't you sell Whitie?" Sepp asked next.

"She must be too old," Kobi answered. "One fellow said that if I get 50 francs for her, there will be black snow."

"Maybe she isn't young," said Sepp, "but she does give a lot of milk."

Whitie was <u>restless</u>. She wanted to be milked. She pulled at the rope with which she was tied.

Just then an old mountain man stepped out from the inn in front of the goat market. His hair had not been cut for a year. He was not very clean. His pants were so <u>patched</u> that Kobi could not tell the <u>patches</u> from the pants or the pants from the patches.

As he saw the two country boys standing beside their goat, he walked up to them. He looked Whitie over. Then he shouted so loudly that many people turned around to listen.

"This must be the goat <u>Noah</u> took with him on the <u>ark</u>!" he shouted.

Sepp answered as quick as a <u>flash</u>.
"Well, those must be Noah's pants you
have on. You should have his goat to
go with them."

Everyone laughed. The old fellow
with the patches said no more but
slipped away quickly in the crowd.
Sepp was proud of having got the
better of him.

"Now, Kobi, what are we going to
do about Whitie? We must find some
way to prove that she is still a good
goat. Oh, I know!" exploded Sepp.

He smiled as the thought came to him.

"Let's milk Whitie," Sepp continued. "When these smart fellows see the milk she gives, that will be a different story."

"A fine idea!" exclaimed Kobi, with a shake of his blond head.

The boys walked back to the cattle market, leaving Whitie tied to the post. At the market they found a farmer milking his restless cow. They waited for him to finish. They asked if they might borrow his bucket.

On their way back to the goat market, the boys forgot about Whitie. They stopped at every stall along the way to see what the people were selling. They talked about the coming summer. Sepp was going with his father's cattle to the mountains, too. His alp was in the same valley as Kobi's alp. They would be only a short walk from each other.

"We can see each other when work is over for the day," said Kobi.

"Yes, and this summer we will learn how to ring the big cowbells," said Sepp, with a pleased smile. "When you ring the cowbells on your alp, I will answer you from mine."

At last the boys were back at the goat market with the bucket. At the very same minute, both of them saw that Whitie had disappeared. She had eaten through the rope with which she had been tied. Only a small piece of rope had been left behind.

A Troublesome Goat

"Whitie has run away! She has run home to be milked!" yelled Kobi.

"Oh, no!" shouted Sepp. "She is somewhere around. People always tie up a runaway animal."

A crowd had gathered in front of one of the stalls. It was a flower stall. All at once the boys heard a woman yell and saw an <u>umbrella</u> going up and down above the heads of the people.

"She must be in there!" cried Kobi.

The boys pushed their way through the crowd as best they could.

Kobi was right. Whitie was there, right in the middle of the red geraniums and the rest of the flowers. A woman was holding Whitie by the broken rope and was <u>pelting</u> her with an umbrella as she cried, "You thieving goat! Where is your master?"

People in the crowd began shouting, "Give it to her, lady, give it to her!"

As Kobi snatched the rope from her, the woman yelled, "Why don't you tie up your goat so that she can't break away? Just see what she has done!"

The woman was so mad that she lifted her umbrella to <u>beat</u> Kobi, too, but Sepp stepped in between them. Sepp was tall for his age, and he was mad, too.

The woman stepped back as Sepp yelled at her, "Don't touch that boy! What are you beating his goat for?"

"Beating his goat for! Beating his
goat for! Listen to him!" cried the
woman, <u>waving</u> her umbrella in the air.
"For eating my flowers, of course. Six
francs' worth she has eaten. The best of
the lot! Look yourself!" And she pointed
to the box of flowers on the ground
at her feet.

Kobi and Sepp looked. Whitie had
not nibbled many flowers, not more than
ten at the most.

"Six francs for that many flowers!" yelled Sepp. "You must think your flowers are made of gold!"

By this time the farmers, standing around and listening in, were laughing loudly. They liked this boy who was standing up to the woman and protecting his smaller friend.

"Go after her, boy! Give it to her!" shouted one mountaineer.

The woman saw that everyone was on Sepp's side. She turned her back on the crowd, talking away to herself in a voice so low that no one else could understand what she said.

"We will play fair with you," called Sepp. "We will milk the goat and give you all her milk. Then you will be well paid for your flowers."

As the crowd started to break up, Kobi handed the broken rope to Sepp and made ready to milk Whitie.

A Friend Indeed

All this time a mountaineer with long white whiskers had been <u>eying</u> the two boys. Now, as Kobi pressed the callus on his thumb against his fingers, and the milk began to hit against the side of the bucket, the farmer stood there looking at him.

After a while the farmer said, "Is your goat a good milker?"

"Yes," answered Kobi. "A very good milker! There is nothing wrong with her except that she is 5 years old."

"What you say is true," said the man, looking down into the bucket. "She is a good milker. How much do you want for her, son?"

"I have been asking 50 francs," said Kobi.

"That is a lot of money for a goat 5 years old," said the farmer, smiling kindly. "Maybe you think she is worth that much because she is your favorite goat—your pet, maybe. I know how boys are. Here are 30 francs. Will you take that? Think it over, son."

Kobi looked up into the kind eyes of the mountaineer. Then all at once he found himself telling the farmer all about Uncle Jacob, all about the goatskin pants, about the red vest with the silver buttons, and about the leather braces which he must earn for himself.

"Now you see why I must sell Whitie," Kobi ended up by saying.

The farmer smiled broadly. Then he said, "I was once a herdboy on the Alps myself. I still remember how wonderful it was to own some black leather braces with brass cows on the crosspiece. You will need a leather cap, too, and some leather straps for your stockings. Then there must be a gold spoon for one ear and a handkerchief for your waist. I'll tell you what I'll do. I'll pay you 40 francs, and then you can buy everything you need. And anyway, I can see that your goat is a good one."

He put 40 francs into Kobi's hand. As he walked away, leading the goat, he turned around once more and said with a big smile, "Next time, son, tie your goat with a stronger rope."

"I will!" shouted Kobi, waving good-by as he and Sepp hurried over to give Whitie's milk to the cross woman in the flower stall.

No sooner had Kobi and Sepp returned the borrowed bucket than they tore down the street to the old cobbler's shop.

Kobi put down 16 francs on the counter, explaining excitedly what he wanted. The cobbler pointed to some braces hanging on the wall. Kobi took them down and stood there, holding them up to the light. They were beautiful. Three brass cows, two herders, and two dogs paraded across the crosspiece, shining like gold.

When the boys left the shop, they had the leather cap and the stocking straps. At the shop next door they found the handkerchief and the gold spoon.

Spring was over at last, and summer was here. One day in early summer a long parade of cows, pigs, goats, wagons, and men was climbing the long trail to the summer pastures in the high Alps.

Far ahead of the others, trying to keep up with six lively goats, was Kobi. His herdboy suit was wonderful, but best of all were his black leather braces.

Wouldn't It Be Wonderful?

It was afternoon in Miss Winters' schoolroom in Redwood City. On a table at the front of the room was a suit box, and beside it a book. On the book's red cover were the words "Kobi, A Boy of Switzerland."

A low knock, and the door opened. There stood Mr. Franz, the janitor. In his hands were some—. But you know. Why should I tell you?

Before the afternoon was over, every boy had a chance to try on the goatskin pants, the vest, and the braces. If the rest of the things which go with a herd-boy suit were missing, no one seemed to care. The important things were still there.

"Wouldn't it be wonderful to be a herdboy in Switzerland?" said Bonny, as the boys and girls left for home.

Everyone agreed with Bonny. Do you?

A Troublesome Fellow

I'm a goat, a troublesome fellow.
This is something
I think you should know.
I eat whatever I want to eat.
I climb where I should not go.

I'm a goat, a troublesome fellow,
With an evil look in my eye.
I do as I please.
I do it with ease.
If you think you can stop me,
Just try.

I'm a goat, a troublesome fellow.
The words I am saying are true.
Have nothing whatever
To do with a goat,
Or you will be troublesome, too.

Wings against the Wind

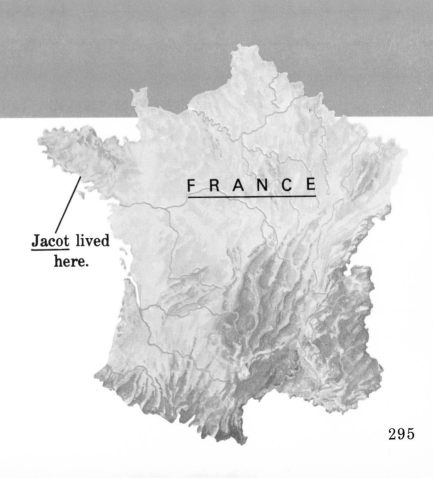

F R A N C E

Jacot lived
here.

Helping Yourself with New Words
Picture Dictionary

barrel

beret (bə rā′)

eggs

sea gull

mast

policeman

priest

sabot (sä bō′)

sailor

Words You Can Get by Yourself

coat	not	roll	more	careless	catch
boat	net	unroll	shore	carelessly	hatch

poor	lass	well	send	men	speak
poorly	less	shell	sand	mend	creak
	bless				creaking
	blessing				

stones	strange	cap	light	wild	low
bones	stranger	flap	lightly	wildly	lower
	strangely	flapped			lowered
		flapping			

296

mean	flash	get	six	speak	real
lean	splash	yet	sixth	sneak	steal

ear	wave	smart	deaf	how	squat
near	save	smarter	deafen	howl	squatted
			deafening	yowl	

car	ar	fold	mind	too	bright
carve	sharp	unfold	remind	fool	brighten
carving	sharper				brightened

ten	lip	shine	all so	feet	new
hen	clip	shiny	also	meet	grew
	clipped	tiny			threw

Two Words Make One Word

moreover fisherman fishermen background seaweed

seashore throughout meantime nearby wrongdoings

henhouse daybreak troublemaker overturn

Let the Sentences Help You

1. Hens lay eggs.
   My hens laid six eggs today.

2. The wave was strong enough to throw me over.
   The boat was thrown up on shore by the waves.

3. I will show pictures of my trip.
   I have shown them to many people.

4. Please ring the bell.
   Please wring the water out of my socks.

Glossary

ac cuse (ə kūz′), to say that someone has done something wrong.
ac cused′

an gry (ang′grē), mad or very much displeased.

ar rest (ə rest′), to take to jail or court because of wrongdoing. **ar rest′ed**

aunt (ant), your father's sister, your mother's sister, or your uncle's wife.

chap el (chap′l), a small church.

cock y (kok′ē), proud; in love with one's self.

com bi na tion (kom′bə nā′shən), two or more people who join to do something together.

cos tume (kos′tüm), a dress or suit.

cow ard (kou′ərd), one who is not brave; one who is afraid.

cri (krē), a sea gull's cry.

deck (dek), the floor of a ship.

few (fū), not many.

France (frans), the name of a country.

Fri poun (frē pün′), a sea gull's name.

heav en (hev′ən), the place where God lives.

Ja cot (zhə kō′), the name of a man.

leap (lēp), to jump. **leaped**

Mar i (mär′ē), the name of a woman.

none (nun), not any.

rob ber (rob′ər), one who steals.

sar dine (sär dēn′), a small fish.

shoul der (shōl′dər), the part of the body to which the arms are fastened.

soft-heart ed (sôft′här′tid), kind.

wear (wãr), to have on one's body.

cap, fāce, cãre, fär; let, bē, wėre; it, īce; hot, ōpen, ôrder; voice, house; cut, pùt, tülip, ūse; th, thing; ᴛʜ, then; zh, garage; ə stands for *a* in about, *e* in angel, *i* in cabin, *o* in wagon, *u* in suppose

A Good Combination

Someday Mark Waters would be an artist. So everyone said. He loved to paint pictures. His favorite pictures were <u>boats</u>. Whenever he painted a boat picture, someone would say, "Mmmmmmmmm, are you keen! How do you do it?"

Then Mark would always answer, "Oh, I don't know. It just comes easy."

Jack Fields had imagination. He could make up stories that would make your hair stand on end. And when he read a story from a book, you forgot that YOU were YOU. You became one of the people he was reading about. He was going to be an actor, or maybe write for TV.

The two boys were a good combination. Moreover, they were buddies.

One day after lunch the boys were almost late for school. When they came hurrying in, Mark had a long roll of paper under his arm, and Jack had a book, on the cover of which were the words "Wings against the Wind." They put the roll and the book on a table at the front of the room, with sideways grins at Miss Winters. A questioning look flashed across the face of everyone else in the room, and John Sun-Yee said right out loud, "What's up?"

"Never you mind," smiled Miss Winters. "You will find out later."

So it was the end of the afternoon when Mark and Jack stood up in front of the room and Mark began to explain.

"My mom's ancestors came from France," he said, pointing to the world map. "Here is my name card."

"I never even saw my great-grand-father," Mark continued. "He was a fisherman, and he was lost at sea. The sails on his boat were bright red, and the nets in which he used to catch fish were blue. My mom told me all about him. I wish I had a fisherman's costume to show you, like the herdboy suit Mr. Franz and Sepp and Kobi used to wear on their way to the mountain pastures. But we haven't one at our house. So I had to do the next best thing. I painted a picture to show how I think my great-grandfather must have looked. We have a picture of him at home, but all it shows is his face. I didn't do such a good job on his face in my picture, but he is dressed right—just the way fishermen do dress in France even today. My mom told me so. Want to see my picture? Here goes!"

Mark and Jack unrolled the picture.

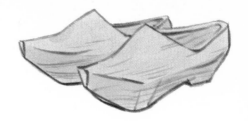

"See this cap?" said Jack, pointing to the cap in the picture. "It's a beret. We have berets in this country, too. These wooden shoes are called sabots. Good for climbing over rocks on the shore! Don't you wish you had some? I do."

"Here are the fishing boats with their different colored sails," Mark broke in, pointing to the boats in the background. "And what do you think? Jack found a book to go with my picture. He will make you think that the hero of the story was really my great-grandfather. Everyone ready? Let's hang up the picture and start."

"Ready!" sounded from every corner of the room, as Jack opened the cover of the book and turned to page 1.

Papa Jacot

One morning in spring a sea <u>gull</u> <u>laid</u> three <u>eggs</u> in her nest on the shore not far from a small fishing village in France. She was a lazy bird that cared little for home life. So her nest was <u>thrown</u> together as <u>carelessly</u> as if the sea had tossed the <u>seaweed</u>, from which it was made, up on the shore.

It was small wonder that, just as the eggs were ready to <u>hatch</u>, one of them went rolling over the side of the <u>poorly</u> made nest. The mother gull did not mind. She followed the egg with her eyes until it came to a stop at the water's edge. Then she lifted her wings and shook her tail as if to say, "One <u>less</u> mouth to feed!"

At that minute a sound could be heard, coming from inside the <u>shell</u>.

A hungry sea gull saw the egg by the water's edge and swooped down beside it. The bird was about to crack the shell and eat the egg when the sound of wooden sabots could be heard coming across the rocks. The gull screeched with disappointment and flew away.

Jacot, a young fisherman, came walking along the shore. He was dressed in a fisherman's costume with a black beret on his head.

"Well, now!" he exclaimed, when he saw the egg. "This is a strange thing to come rolling in upon the waves."

He dropped the egg into his pocket and went on his way, climbing over rocks and walking through sand until he came at last to his fishing boat. Before long he was busily at work helping other fishermen mend the holes in the blue fishing nets.

Jacot had been working only a short while when he heard a creaking sound. He looked puzzled. First he moved his arms, then his back, then his legs.

"I must be getting old before my time," he said to the fishermen working with him. "My bones are creaking like the floors in an old house."

Later, when he put his hand into his pocket, he let out a surprised cry. His fingers had touched something soft and wet. He lifted out a baby sea gull, white with black spots on its back.

"Heaven help me!" yelled Jacot. "Look! I have hatched a sea gull!"

The other fishermen laughed and danced and hit Jacot on the back.

"Jacot is the papa of a sea gull!" they all shouted.

One fisherman, who could always smell trouble coming, was the first to stop laughing and dancing.

"You are borrowing trouble," he told Jacot. "Your gull will eat our sardines as fast as we catch them. Get rid of him."

Jacot was a soft-hearted fellow, but stubborn, too. As he returned the baby gull to his pocket, he said.

"This funny little fellow is mine, and I am going to keep him. He will sail with me each time I go out fishing. And when we go to the <u>Blessing</u> of the Sea, he will sit on my <u>shoulder</u>."

Each year, in the fishing villages in France, there is a festival day. On this day a <u>priest</u> comes down to the <u>seashore</u> to <u>bless</u> the fishing boats with their bright-colored sails and their blue nets. He prays for their safe return from every fishing trip they may take <u>throughout</u> the year. This was the festival day Jacot was thinking about.

So it happened that a baby sea gull found a home on Jacot's fishing boat. He soon became a lively fellow. He did not eat ALL the sardines in the fishermen's nets—just enough to keep him alive and happy. In return, he paid his own way.

Who Can't Swim?

When any <u>stranger</u> tried to step foot on the boat, <u>Fripoun</u>, the baby sea gull, would <u>flap</u> his wings, stretch out his neck, and cry, "<u>Cri</u>, cri, cri!" He seemed to be trying to say, "Don't come a step farther, or it will be the end of you. Cri, cri, cri!"

One day, before his long feathers were all grown in, Fripoun tumbled off the side of the boat into the water.

"Cri, cri, cri!" he screeched, beating the water with his wings. His head went under.

It was lucky that Jacot was there to fish him out with a hand net.

"He almost drowned!" cried Jacot. "What kind of gull is this? He can't even swim."

"Once I saw some young gulls in the water for the first time," explained one of the fishermen. "The father and mother gulls were swooping down beside them to tell them what to do. What kind of papa are you that you have not shown Fripoun how to swim?"

Jacot waited until the gull had his first grown-up coat of gray feathers mixed with brown. Then he put some sea water into a tank on deck. He placed Fripoun lightly upon the water. The gull kicked, and flapped his wings.

"No, no!" said Jacot. "Do not kick the water. Push it back with your feet and lift your head. That is the way."

Once Fripoun stopped flapping his wings wildly, he sailed as easily as if he had been swimming all his life.

Next Jacot lowered Fripoun into the blue waters of the sea. The gull began at once to swim. Jacot was so excited that he leaned too far over the side of the boat. Splash, splash! He was in the water with Fripoun—in the water flapping his arms and kicking his legs.

"Help! Help!" yelled Jacot, for, like so many sailors, he had never learned to swim.

Two fishermen pulled Jacot from the water with the sea running out of his nose and mouth.

So that is how Fripoun learned to swim from a papa who did not know how to swim himself.

Robber Six-Toes

Fripoun had not <u>yet</u> learned to fly. He could lift his wings and flap across the deck, but that was all.

One afternoon the fishing boat returned to shore with a great catch of fish. The fishermen packed the fish in baskets and then lifted the baskets into a two-wheeled cart to take them to market.

"No, you cannot go," insisted Jacot, as he chased Fripoun back onto the deck for the <u>sixth</u> time. "Stay here and take care of the boat. Let no one come on deck while we are gone. Keep your eye on the fish we have left behind for our own dinner."

After the fishermen left, Fripoun sat on the end of the boat with his head turned into the wind.

While Fripoun sat there, a six-toed cat came toeing along the sands.

The cat looked as if she were old enough to have been with Noah on the ark. Her hair was coming out in patches. All her life she had made her living by <u>sneaking</u> from village to village, <u>stealing</u> from the fishing boats.

Robber Six-Toes saw Jacot's boat. She smelled the fish. But, better yet, she saw a bird sitting on the end of the boat with his head turned into the wind. This gray one would make a good dinner. Six-Toes gave a big <u>leap</u> and landed on deck on all fours. One more half-leap, and she would have the bird.

A feeling down inside Fripoun told
him that danger was near. Just as the
cat was about to make her half-leap,
he flapped his way to the front of the
boat. Now Fripoun was afraid—very
much afraid indeed. His wings beat
faster and faster. Strangely enough, the
faster he beat his wings, the stronger
they seemed to become. Up, up into
the air they carried him until he was
flying out over the water. Soon he
returned to sit on top of the mast. He
looked down on the evil one. From
up here the cat looked very small and
very harmless.

Robber Six-Toes was as mad and disgusted as a cat could get. Her green eyes turned from side to side. Then she saw the fish. Her mouth opened, her whiskers waved, as she made ready to leap.

Fripoun, up on the mast, was no longer afraid. His wings were strong enough to protect him from the evil one. He must <u>save</u> Jacot's fish. Down he swooped, sailing right over the cat's back.

"Cri, cri, cri!" he screeched, almost in her ear. "Cri, cri, cri!"

Robber Six-Toes was really a coward. Her thieving ways had made her that way. She always ran from anyone stronger and smarter than herself. So now, with a deafening yowl, she leaped on shore and disappeared behind a barrel and a pile of rope outside the cobbler shop. From time to time she peeped out.

Before long she could be seen stealing as quietly as a shadow over the rocks. From the boat next to Jacot's, she helped herself to a fish. On another boat she found duck eggs. From every boat she took something. She had made up her mind to stay for a time in this village where living came so easy.

In the meantime, Fripoun was trying his wings. He went swooping out over the water and back again. He had learned to fly from a cat that could not fly a flap herself.

Once Jacot returned from market, he squatted down on deck, took out a knife, and began carving a piece of wood.

"Cri, cri, cri!" squawked the gull to let Jacot know that he had chased the six-toed robber away forever.

"What's wrong? Why carry on so?" said Jacot. "Soon I shall take you to the chapel for the Blessing of the Sea. You shall sit on my shoulder. So stop your squawking."

"At the Blessing of the Sea he will squawk and flap until people drive you away with sticks and stones," laughed a fisherman. "Tell me. What are you carving?"

"It's a secret," grinned Jacot. "Don't you wish you knew?"

"Wondering about it won't keep me awake nights," joked the fisherman. "It looks to me like a sabot for a one-legged sailor without any toes."

Fripoun Must Go

Little did Fripoun know how much trouble that black cat would bring down upon his head in the days to come.

Whenever the fishing boats returned to shore, the cat was there waiting, taking care to keep herself well hidden.

Fripoun's eyes were <u>sharper</u> than those of men. One day when the gull was on the wing, he saw Robber Six-Toes helping herself to a fish on a <u>nearby</u> boat.

Fripoun had never been so <u>angry</u>. He had thought that he was rid of that cat forever. He screeched and squawked and flew at her. The cat leaped back on shore, leaving behind her a half-eaten fish.

A fisherman on the boat turned to see what was happening. The cat had disappeared. All he could see was Fripoun flying above the half-eaten fish. He lost no time in calling on Jacot.

"Your sea gull is stealing fish from the other boats," he told Jacot.

"How can that be?" said Jacot. "We have missed no fish from this boat except those I gave him myself."

"That proves it," insisted the fisherman. "He does not steal from his own boat, for then he would be found out. But he helped himself to one of my fish. I saw him do it."

Jacot was a stubborn fellow. He would not believe what the man said. But from that time on, Fripoun was blamed for all the cat's wrongdoings.

"Evil one!" shouted the fishermen up and down the shore. "You bring bad luck. Go to sea where you belong."

Soon everything that disappeared was blamed on Fripoun, even things which no gull would want or could fly away with.

A sailor's lass lost her cap and the handkerchief she liked to wear at her waist. A spoon and an umbrella disappeared. Someone else lost the sabots he had left on the rocks to dry in the sun. Even far out at sea, fishermen <u>accused</u> Fripoun of stealing fish from their blue nets. All trails seemed to lead to Jacot's sea gull.

"Let me catch him, and I will <u>wring</u> his neck," said one fisherman.

"Who wrings my gull's neck must wring mine first!" exploded Jacot.

As days went by, Jacot knew that he must get rid of Fripoun. But how could he do it without wringing the gull's neck—and that he would not do!

One day a <u>policeman</u> stood on shore, waiting for Jacot's boat to arrive.

The minute the policeman stepped on deck, Fripoun flew at him, squawking and flapping, "Cri, cri, cri!"

"No, no!" said Jacot, taking Fripoun under his arm. "One does not do that to a Master Policeman. Only to fishermen and sardines! Master Policeman is a very important man."

Master Policeman knew very well how important he was. He <u>unfolded</u> a paper and started right in to read.

"One sea gull belonging to Fisherman Jacot is accused of stealing. Said fisherman is ordered to get rid of said sea gull at once. Otherwise, he will be arrested."

"But, Master Policeman," begged Jacot, "I have counted on taking my gull to the Blessing of the Sea the day after tomorrow. Let me keep him until then. It will give me time to think of something to do with him."

The policeman stood up tall and looked down his nose at Jacot.

"The order I read said AT ONCE," he barked. "Not tomorrow! Not the day after! AT ONCE!"

The policeman stepped back on shore and paraded off through the village. Jacot followed him with his eyes.

"He and his cocky airs!" said Jacot. "He reminds me of my Aunt Mari's big red rooster."

"What does your aunt's rooster have to do with it?" asked a fisherman. "Paint Fripoun red and make believe he is a rooster, and you will <u>fool</u> no one but yourself."

All at once Jacot's face <u>brightened</u>.

"It is Fripoun we will fool!" he exclaimed. "I will take Fripoun to my uncle's farm on the other side of town. He can live with Aunt Mari's <u>hens</u> and roosters. It will be a good home for him. After a while—this is the way it will be—Fripoun will think that he is a rooster."

"But what about the Blessing of the Sea?" asked the fisherman.

"I will keep my word," said Jacot. "Aunt Mari and I will make plans."

Fripoun stretched his wings and flew high into the air. It was a good thing Aunt Mari was not here. What would she think of this flying rooster?

Clipped Wings

The sun was not yet up the next morning when Jacot left the water front with a basket of fish on his arm and Fripoun on his shoulder. He walked through the streets of the village, where fishing nets were hanging from the upper-story windows of the tall stone houses. Soon he was on his way to Uncle Jacot's farm.

When he arrived, Aunt Mari was leaning on the hen-yard gate. She was a busy little old lady with sharp blue eyes and a merry smile. She could not believe her eyes when she saw Jacot.

"Our Jacot!" she cried. "But at what market did you buy such a bird?"

Of course, Jacot had to explain about the sea gull. He ended by saying, "So everyone is angry with me. The policeman said I must get rid of the gull."

"What!" said Aunt Mari, her eyes flashing. "I should like to have that policeman come near me and tell me what to do with my hens. Poor harmless creatures! I would give him something to burn his ears."

Jacot explained that one did not talk back to a policeman and that Fripoun had to have a new home.

"He may stay if my hens like him," said Aunt Mari. "Otherwise not!"

"There is only one thing I ask of you," begged Jacot. "Bring him with you to the Blessing of the Sea tomorrow. I want him to ride on my shoulder."

"Indeed I will," agreed Aunt Mari.

"Now shall we shut him up in the henhouse?" asked Jacot.

Aunt Mari shook her head. "We cannot shut him up. He would be unhappy and make my hens unhappy, too."

"But he will fly away if he is left in the hen yard," said Jacot. "He will fly back to my fishing boat. Then some fisherman will wring his neck."

"That shows how little you know about feathered creatures," said Aunt Mari. "I will clip one wing, and that will keep his feet on the ground."

Jacot looked surprised and uneasy.

"Nothing to have a long face about," laughed Aunt Mari. "I clip just a few feathers from one wing. A few feathers more or less will not harm him. They will grow in again. But for a while, he cannot fly. Maybe by the time other feathers grow in, we can fool him into believing that he is a rooster."

By this time, Uncle Jacot had come in from the fields. While Jacot did his best to hold on to the gull, his uncle pulled out the gull's wing. Another second, and a few gray feathers fell on the ground.

"Cri, cri, cri!" squawked poor Fripoun. "Cri, cri, cri!"

Aunt Mari opened the gate of the hen yard and pushed the gull inside.

The hen yard did not please Fripoun. It did not roll like the deck of a boat. It was not slippery with sardines. He lifted his wings to fly out, only to tumble over on his back. Again and again and again he tried.

"No," said Jacot. "Your flying days are over. Hens do not fly, and they are very happy. You will be happy, too. Soon you will forget the sea and believe that you are a rooster, too."

Fripoun sat on the ground like a gray rock. Even when Jacot laid his hand on Fripoun's head, the gull did not move. Jacot smoothed the gull's soft feathers and then walked quickly away. The hens and the red rooster came to look the newcomer over, but Fripoun turned his back on them. Never had he been so unhappy, not since the day he was hatched from the egg in Jacot's pocket.

When the hens and the rooster went back into the henhouse for the night, Fripoun did not join them. He put his head under his wing and went to sleep.

At <u>daybreak</u> the next morning the red rooster came out of the henhouse and crowed loud and long. Fripoun pulled his head from under his wing to look at Master Red Cock.

Once he was through crowing, the red rooster made up his mind that he did not want this strange creature in the hen yard. He flapped his wings and ran at Fripoun. Fripoun came to life with a squawk. Soon gray feathers, brown feathers, and red feathers were flying all over the hen yard.

Out of the farmhouse flew Aunt Mari with a bucket of water in her hand. She was shouting and splashing water as she ran.

Now, maybe Master Red Cock was a coward. Maybe he did not like water, as the sea gull did. Anyway, he went racing back into the henhouse.

"That policeman was right!" shouted Aunt Mari at poor Fripoun. "You are nothing but a troublemaker. A rooster and a sea gull are a bad combination. Indeed I WILL take you to the Blessing of the Sea. Jacot can keep you and make you mend your ways. You cannot stay here to make my rooster unhappy."

Fripoun sat on the ground like a gray rock. When Master Red Cock came sneaking out into the hen yard with the hens, Fripoun did not look up.

The Blessing of the Sea

Later that morning Jacot's uncle and
Aunt Mari started for the festival in
their two-wheeled cart.

Uncle Jacot was dressed in his festival
costume. Today he was not wearing a
beret. On his head was a little round
hat with ribbons hanging down the
back. Aunt Mari looked very handsome
in her black dress. Her white cap
looked like a big duck sitting on her
head.

Fripoun sat on the high side of the
cart, his head turned into the wind.

"Sit there and make believe you are on a boat," laughed Uncle Jacot.

It WAS something like riding in a boat. The creaking cart went up and down hill. Green fields rolled away like green waves. Sometimes a house went by, like another boat on the green, rolling waves.

People came flocking down the road in carts, on bicycles, and on foot. Everyone was on his way to the shore and to the chapel which stood there. Uncle Jacot stopped the cart near the water's edge.

"We must find Jacot at once," he said, as he got down from the cart and took Fripoun under his arm.

When his aunt and uncle found Jacot, one look at their faces showed Jacot that something was very wrong. Fripoun squawked loudly as Jacot put the sea gull on his shoulder.

"Is something wrong?" asked Jacot. "Don't the hens like Fripoun?"

Aunt Mari made a thin nose.

"My rooster and your gull hate each other!" she exploded. "After all, my rooster was there first. He has his rights."

In the meantime, Fripoun was stretching his neck toward something Jacot was holding under his arm. It was a tiny little boat, a very beautiful one, which Jacot had carved from that piece of wood. Two red sails were fastened to the stick masts, and on the end of the boat, his head turned into the wind, was a tiny sea gull.

"It is beautiful!" exclaimed Aunt Mari, when Jacot showed it to her.

"But why have you carved a boat to hang in the chapel now?" Aunt Mari continued. "You have not been saved from the sea, and we hope you will never need to be."

In France it is an old custom for a fisherman who has been saved from drowning to <u>carve</u> a tiny boat to hang on some chapel wall. It is his way of giving thanks for being saved from the sea.

"I am not one to wait until I have been almost drowned before I ask for help," explained Jacot. "Better to hang my boat in the chapel before there is danger. It is well that Fripoun is on my boat, too. If he cannot stay with you, he must be protected <u>also</u>."

By this time a long line of singing people was moving down to the water's edge. Jacot and his aunt and uncle hurried to join them.

The priest walked out to <u>meet</u> the incoming waves. He blessed the sea and the men who sailed upon it and the creatures that lived in it.

Jacot shut his eyes and moved his lips slowly.

"Heaven protect us," he whispered, "because the sea is so big and our boats are so small." Then he added a prayer of his own. "And please protect Fripoun because he belongs to the sea."

When prayers were over, the crowd walked into the stone chapel. Fripoun sat quietly on Jacot's shoulder while Jacot added his boat to the others which were hanging there.

Return of the Evil One

Jacot did not return to his boat that night. A friendly sailor stopped him as he was walking along the sands.

"That hard-shell policeman was here a minute ago," the sailor said to Jacot. "I have a feeling in my bones that he is looking for you."

Jacot found an old barrel standing on its side near a dark doorway. He crawled into the barrel and pulled up his legs to make a nest for the gull, and there they stayed for the night.

Before anyone was awake the next morning, Jacot hid Fripoun under his coat. Then, with his sabots in his hand, he slipped quietly along the sand. He made no noise as he stepped down onto the deck of his boat.

Then—a deafening yowl broke the stillness of the morning. A black creature raced across the deck.

Jacot had come to the boat on such quiet cat's feet that Robber Six-Toes had been taken by surprise.

Jacot <u>threw</u> one of his sabots at her. She tried to leap from the boat, but he stood in her way. He threw the other sabot. With a yowl, she leaped for the mast and started up. Up, up she went to the very top.

"Robber! Evil one!" yelled Jacot with all his might. "You are the one who has been stealing from the boats. Here are the half-eaten fish to prove it."

Fripoun worked his way out of the coat and looked up at the yowling cat. He squawked and flapped and tried to fly. In sea gull talk he ordered the cat to leave the boat at once.

The yelling, the yowling, and the squawking waked the water front. More and more fishermen joined Jacot on deck. With them came the policeman.

"Now which one do you <u>accuse</u> of stealing?" yelled Jacot, pointing to the top of the mast. "Did I not catch her in the act? Find her owner, Master Policeman, and <u>arrest</u> him."

Since the cat belonged to no one, how could the policeman do that? He looked a little less cocky as he walked away.

It would be hard to count the ways in which the fishermen tried to get Robber Six-Toes down from that mast. She was a wise one. She knew when she was safe. She would not budge.

At last the other fishing boats went about their business and put out to sea. Only Jacot's boat was left behind.

"We must get rid of that black one before we sail," said Jacot. "She will bring us bad luck. We will catch no fish, and our boat may overturn."

"Let's leave her where she is and go on shore," said one fisherman who sailed with Jacot. "She may come down of her own accord."

Fripoun would not leave the boat. He could not fly, but he could squawk up at the hated cat.

Robber Six-Toes waited until there was no one on deck but the gull. Her green eyes had told her that there was something wrong with Fripoun. Slowly she started down the mast. Just as she was in the air, about to leap onto the gull's back, Fripoun hit her with his clipped wing.

The cat was taken by surprise and lost her footing. Splash she went over the side of the boat into the water.

The next minute she was swimming wildly for shore. Soon, with her wet tail flying, she went racing down the rocky shore. That was the last the village ever saw of Robber Six-Toes.

As for Fripoun, only good things happened to him in the days ahead. His gray and brown feathers fell out. His wing feathers <u>grew</u> in again. Now he was white with a few blue-gray feathers on his shoulders and a few black feathers on the ends of his wings. By day he went riding the air out over the sea with the other gulls. At night he sat on the end of Jacot's boat with his head turned into the wind.

What I Love to Do

I love
To sit in a boat
Far out on a lake
When the sun comes up
And I'm half awake.

I may catch one fish.
I may catch none.
But fishing with Dad,
Oh, that's what's fun.

G H A N A

Jack's ancestors came from here.

Why Spiders Hide in Dark Corners

Helping Yourself with New Words
Picture Dictionary

banana tree

circle

spider

tomatoes

tree bear

tree frog

Words You Can Get by Yourself

ride	thought	trade	cart	bus
hide	thoughtful	trader	Carter	buses
hiding				
fool	plum	backward	call	strange
stool	drum	afterward	recall	change
				changed
				unchanged
hero	imagination	life	new	big
heroes	imagine	wife	stew	biggest
ripe	knife	head	saw	stick
ripest	knives	dead	straw	sticky
luck	hope	rag	dark	far
stuck	hoping	drag	darkest	star
		dragged		starlight

Two Words Make One Word

grasslands   airfields   drumbeat

firelight   underground   headman

Glossary

Af ri ca (af′rə kə), a continent, one of the large masses of land on the earth.

Af ri can (af′rə kən), of or belonging to the continent of Africa.

bees wax (bēz′waks′), a sticky substance given out by bees, used in making their honeycombs.

breath (breth), air drawn into and out of the lungs.

butt (but), to hit with one's head.
        but′ted

co coa (kō′kō), a drink made from the ground seeds of the cocoa tree.

dis guise (dis gīz′), a change in one's looks to hide the way one really looks.

en joy (en joi′), to be happy with.
        en joyed′   en joy′ing
             en joy′a ble

folk (fōk), people.

folk tale (fōk tāl), a story made by many people and handed down from father to son.

for est (fôr′ist), deep woods.

Gha na (gä′nə), a country in West Africa.

hun dred (hun′drəd), ten tens.
        hun′dreds

in ter est ing (in′tər is ting), good enough to hold one's attention.

ma gi cian (mə jish′ən), someone who seems to make impossible things happen.

thief (thēf), one who steals.

cap, fāce, cãre, fär; let, bē, wėre; it, īce; hot, ōpen, ôrder; voice, house;
cut, pùt, tülip, ūse; th, thing; ŦH, then; zh, garage; ə stands for a in about,
e in angel, i in cabin, o in wagon, u in suppose

345

A Dad to Help You

Jack Fields had a problem. It may seem a tiny one to you, but it didn't to Jack. For days he had heard everyone in the schoolroom talk about the country from which his ancestors had come. Everyone had found a story to go with his country. Everyone but Jack! He couldn't find a story anywhere. But he wasn't going to give up. Not if he could help it!

Jack remembered the day Mark had come to school with that world map. On that day Jack had asked his dad about his own ancestors. Dad had smiled at him with a thoughtful look, as he said.

"Come to think of it, Jack, your ancestors have been Americans for many, many, many years. They may have been Americans long before the ancestors of some of the boys and girls in your room came to this country.

"Of course, you know," his dad went on, "our ancestors in the first place came from Africa. Let me show you on the map the part of Africa from which they came, the country now called Ghana. I'm sorry, but your mom and I have been so busy just being Americans that we have not taken time to find out about our African ancestors. Maybe you and I can do that. Suppose we start by looking in books."

So Jack and his dad looked. They DID find out many things about Ghana. They read about the gold mines and the traders who came by sea and by land to trade their goods for gold. They read about the miles and miles of grasslands and the animals that came to feed there. They found out that the cocoa which Jack liked may have come from Ghana.

All these things and many more they found out, but what Jack wanted was a story. That he did not find.

A few days later Jack's dad came home
with two tickets in his hand.

"Don't give up yet," he said to Jack.
"I heard today that a well-known speaker
is coming to town to talk about his visit
to Africa. The part of Africa he will
talk about is Ghana. You and I have the
tickets. He may have the story."

Jack was surprised at how <u>interesting</u>
the speaker turned out to be. Mr. <u>Carter</u>
made you see in your mind's eye not only
how Ghana had looked <u>hundreds</u> of years
ago, but also how it looks today. He
made you see not only the little villages
and farms, but also the cities with their
busy streets, their cars and <u>buses</u>, and
their <u>airfields</u>.

At the end the speaker threw aside his coat and put on a long, bright-colored robe.

As he sat down on a low <u>stool</u>, facing all the people, he began to beat softly on an African <u>drum</u>. The room grew very quiet. To the music of the <u>drumbeat</u>, he told an old African story which, he said, had been told in Ghana for hundreds of years, and which was still being told there today.

Afterward Jack could hardly <u>recall</u> a
word he had said as he walked forward
with his dad to meet the speaker. He
must have said something because Mr.
Carter looked pleased and said he would
send Jack a book with the story in it.

All Jack remembered saying was, "I'll
read it until I know it by heart. Then
I can tell it as you told it tonight."

Jack had a warm feeling deep down
inside of him all the way home.

"You know, Dad," he said with a very
thoughtful look, "since everything that
Mr. Carter said is true, we can be very
proud of our ancestors. Don't you think
so?"

"Yes, I do, Jack," said his dad. "And
that's something all of us should remember, and none of us should forget."

First Things First

From then on, Jack raced home from school each day to find out what the postman had left for him. Mark and David raced along with him.

"That man was just fooling you," David insisted, as the days went by. "He didn't mean to send that book. It was too much trouble." But Jack thought otherwise.

One day when everyone else had given up hope, Jack raced home all by himself. There was the book with the story. Clipped to the cover was a piece of paper which explained what Jack should do before he told the story. It also told what he should do afterward. The afterward part made Jack grin as he thought to himself:

"That's something to remember. I won't say a thing about that until my story is finished. Then some people I know will have to do some guessing."

On the very next day, when the good news became known, everyone thought he would hear that story. Jack had a different idea. He had to learn that story by heart, didn't he? That took time. Then, too, he had to tease his mom to make something. There was another little thing he had to do also.

At last he was ready—almost. He had learned many things from Mr. Carter, and he was feeling very important. He looked around the room as if he knew all there was to know about everything.

"My story will be different from those you have been hearing because it is a folk tale," Jack began by saying.

"The word 'folk' means people. The story I am going to tell you is hundreds and hundreds of years old. It may have been told in the villages of Ghana in Africa before my ancestors or anyone else in the world could read or write.

"When the men of a village came home from work each night, they sat down to rest in the firelight. The other people in the village gathered round them. Those who liked best to tell stories became the storytellers. They told their tales to those who liked best to listen. Many different people had a part in making up the stories. That is why they have come to be called 'people's stories,' or folk tales. That is the way it happened, and that is the way Mr. Carter explained it to me.

"Folk tales are stories that never die," Jack went on to explain. "I'll tell you why. When fathers and mothers in Ghana heard a good folk tale, they retold it to their children. These children remembered it when they grew up and told it to their children. Their children did the same. So the folk tales went on living and were not forgotten.

"Storytellers in Ghana today still tell the same old tales. The stories have <u>changed</u> somewhat as they have traveled down through the years. But in most ways they are the same old stories.

"The same thing has happened all over the world," Jack continued. "People from every country have their own folk tales. The people of Mexico have theirs. The Japanese have theirs. The American Indians have their own folk tales.

"When people learned to read and write, their folk tales were written down and made into books. Many such books can be found today in France and Italy. There are books of English folk tales also. Folk stories are very <u>enjoyable</u> when you read them out of books. They are even more enjoyable when, in the way of the old storytellers, they are told aloud.

"There is one last thing you should know. Many folk tales have animals for <u>heroes</u>. The animals talk and act so much like people that they make you believe they are really people in <u>disguise</u>.

"In Ghana," Jack ended by saying, "many folk tales are about a strange creature called Spider. He is supposed to be a spider, but he acts like a man. He loves to eat, and he hates to work. He thinks he is wise, but at times he is stupid. My story is just one of many stories about Spider. Each tale explains why something happens. Why the moon is in the sky! Why the turtle has a hard shell! My story will tell you why spiders hide in dark corners."

By this time, Jack had done so much explaining that his story had to be put off until another day.

Imagination at Work

The next afternoon every boy and girl in the room wondered what was going on as Jack pulled down the shades on all the windows. He disappeared for a time and came back dressed in a bright-colored robe. He had a low stool in one hand and the drum which he had borrowed from the boy next door in the other hand.

"It has to be as dark as we can make it," he explained, "because these stories were told only at night when the work of the day was over.

"Now sit in a circle around me," he ordered, "and get your imaginations to work. Imagine that you are in a village in Ghana hundreds of years ago. The moon is high in the sky. The mothers, who have finished their work for the day, walk toward the open place in the village where people sit and talk.

"The last cooking fire has gone out.
The last jar of water has been carried
from the river. The moon is so bright
that people can see each others' faces.

"The forest behind the village is tall
and dark. The tree bears screech, and the
tree frogs croak. The animals in the
deep forest walk softly, and their eyes
shine in the growing darkness.

"Inside the village the little round houses stand in a circle. Inside the circle is a fire. The people laugh and are happy. Their voices are low and sound like music.

"The men, who have been sitting off by themselves, walk to the storytelling place. Their bright-colored robes wave from their shoulders, like sails in the wind, as they walk. Children, who have been playing with small fishing boats like their fathers', run to join the circle. Tiny babies sleep safely on their mothers' backs.

"The storyteller is a tall, black man with a sparkle in his eye. He walks slowly forward to place a low stool in the middle of the circle near the fire. As he sits down and crosses his long legs, he looks far away into the night, thinking about which story he will tell first. Everyone waits.

" 'Tell us a story about Spider,' " the
children cry, to break the stillness.

" 'Yoo-oo-oo,' " answer the people. That
means that they want a Spider story, too.

" 'Once upon a time,' " the storyteller
will say, as he looks around him.

And "Once upon a time" was the way
Jack began his story, beating softly on
his drum.

Spider's Plan

Once upon a time Spider lived with his
<u>wife</u> and his two sons in a house made
of <u>banana</u> leaves. Not far away was the
forest where the cocoa trees grew.

Behind the banana-leaf house was a
garden. In it Spider and his wife planted
many vegetables. Orange and banana
trees grew around its edges.

When the rains came each year, the
vegetables grew, and the garden was
green and beautiful. The oranges and
bananas ripened, and Spider and his
family had all they wanted to eat.

Each day Spider's wife cooked rice and fish and vegetables and other good things in her big cooking pot. The smell of that wonderful stew made Spider's mouth water. Each day Spider went on eating until he could eat no more.

You might have thought that Spider would be satisfied with the way things were going, but he wasn't. Every day, as soon as the stew had disappeared, he looked around to find something for his wife to cook next. He wanted to eat most of the time when he wasn't sleeping.

As the days went by, something began to trouble Spider.

"Things are not as they should be around here," he said to himself one morning. "Of all the good things in my garden, the very best things should be ONLY for me. I must think of a way to save the best things for myself. My family can get along with the next best."

So Spider sat down under a banana tree in the garden to think. At last he hit upon a great idea. He began at once to carry out his plan.

First he hung his head down low. Next he made believe that he could hardly walk, as he made his way back to the banana-leaf house.

"Something is wrong with me," he said to his wife. "I am not feeling well. I am very sick indeed, and I must wait no longer. I must go to the village to see the magician. Since he is wise enough to know what will happen tomorrow, next week, or even next year, he will know what is wrong with me."

"I will go with you to help you on your way," said his wife, looking at him sadly with tears in her eyes.

"You must stay where you are," insisted Spider. "If I do not come by myself, the magician will be angry."

The day was almost over before Spider
returned home. His wife and his two
sons were waiting near the doorway.

"My dear wife and my two sons," said
Spider, shaking his head and looking as
if the world had come to an end, "I have
bad news for you. The magician tells me
that I am very sick. No one can do
anything to help me. Soon I am going
to die and leave you."

"Die and leave us?" cried his wife and
his two sons. "That cannot be."

It took time, but at last Spider made his family understand that what was to be would be. He was going to die, and there was nothing they could do about it.

"Since I am about to die," he went on to explain, "these are the things you must do for me so that I will be happy in the next world.

"First you must dig a deep hole in the garden. Come, and I will show you. Put it here next to the spot where the <u>biggest</u> and <u>ripest</u> <u>tomatoes</u> are growing."

Spider liked tomatoes best of all the good things that grew in his garden.

"Next you must find a box to put me in," he continued. "It must be big and have a cover that is easy to lift. Place the box in the hole, and into it put some spoons and <u>knives</u> and cooking pots so that I can feed myself in the next world."

Spider's wife and his two sons carried out each order carefully.

One day, not long after this, Spider stretched out on the ground in the sun. He shut his eyes and did not move. He remembered to hold his <u>breath</u> when anyone came near him. In every way, he made believe that he was <u>dead</u>. But, of course, he wasn't.

Spider's sons, trying hard to hold back their tears, raced to the village to tell all his friends the bad news.

In no time at all, Spider's friends were at the door of the banana-leaf house.

Carefully they lifted Spider from the ground and placed him in the box beside the tomato patch. When the cover was back on the box and the hole covered lightly with straw, they stood in a circle around the hole in the garden. They sang, and they prayed, and they beat on their drums. Everyone told how much he would miss Spider. Everyone was sad.

Spider did not mind spending the day in his box underground. He found it very enjoyable. He loved to sleep, and he enjoyed thinking of the joke he was playing on everyone.

Night came. Spider's friends had gone home to the village. His wife and sons were asleep in the banana-leaf house. The full moon was high in the sky. Everything in the garden was quiet.

Can you guess what Spider did then?

Very quietly he lifted the cover of the box. Very quietly he pushed aside the straw which covered the hole and peeped out. He looked around to see that all was safe. When he saw that everyone was in bed, he crawled out very slowly.

The moon was so bright that Spider could see everything in the garden. First he helped himself to the best tomatoes. He helped himself to all the best vegetables growing in the garden.

Even then Spider did not stop. He helped himself to the ripest oranges and bananas. He ended up by going to the hen yard at the back of the garden and helping himself to a fine fat rooster.

When he had everything he needed, Spider crawled back into his box and cooked himself a fine dinner. He went on eating for the rest of the night.

The moon disappeared, and the sun came up. Spider did not see what was happening. His full stomach had made him very sleepy. He went on sleeping all through the next day.

The next night, and the next, and the next Spider carried out his plan. How he was enjoying himself! What good things he had to eat in those nighttime dinners! How he was enjoying his daytime sleeps! What fun it was to fool everyone!

Someone Else Has a Plan

All this time something else was going on which Spider knew nothing about.

Each morning Spider's wife walked out to look her garden over. Each morning she saw that something was very wrong. A thief was stealing her best vegetables. The best oranges and bananas were missing from the trees. Her best rooster had disappeared from the hen yard. She must think of a way to catch that thief. She must catch him right away.

She sat down on a low stool by the door of the banana-leaf house to think. She, too, hit upon a grand idea.

First she gathered a great pile of straw. Out of the straw, she and her two sons made a man that looked just like a real man. After that they got a bucket of soft, sticky beeswax and covered the straw man from head to foot. They put him in the middle of the tomato patch.

That night, as soon as everyone was asleep, Spider crawled out of his <u>hiding</u> place. He was just about to help himself to a ripe tomato when he saw a man standing in the middle of HIS garden. He forgot all about being quiet.

"Who are you?" he shouted. "What are you doing in my garden?"

The man did not try to explain. He just stood.

"So you won't talk!" cried Spider. "I'll see about that. I'll <u>change</u> your mind for you."

Still the straw man said nothing.

As he had always done, Spider acted so much like a real man that you might have thought he was a real man in disguise.

"Do you think I am fooling?" he yelled, and with that he hit the straw man with his right hand. His hand stuck fast in the beeswax. Pull as hard as he could, he could not pull his hand away.

"You think you are smart! I'll show you!" screeched Spider. With that, he hit the straw man with his left hand, and that stuck fast, too.

"Do you think you can get the better of me?" yelled Spider. He gave a mighty kick with his right foot, and his foot stuck to the straw man, too.

"Let me go!" he screeched. "Haven't you learned anything yet? Well then, I'll have to give you another kick."

Spider kicked the straw man with his left foot, and that foot stuck, too.

"I'll show you yet!" he shouted, and he butted the straw man with his head. His head stuck in the beeswax also.

Even then Spider didn't give up. He pushed against the straw man with all his might until his stomach was stuck fast also. There he was, stuck in the beeswax from head to foot.

The next morning his wife and his two sons came out to the garden, hoping to catch the thief. Imagine their surprise when they saw Spider stuck to the straw man. At once they understood everything.

"Thief! Thief!" cried his wife and sons,
as they pulled Spider away from the
straw man. "Thief! Thief!" they yelled,
as they <u>dragged</u> him along with them
down to the village.

Soon everyone knew who the thief was.
The people laughed at Spider and made
up funny songs about him.

Just as the magician was about to <u>drag</u>
him before the <u>headman</u> of the village
to see what should be done with him,
Spider broke away from the crowd.

He crawled into a nearby house. He crawled up into the darkest corner under the roof to hide. And he has lived there ever since. And that is why, even today, spiders like to hide in dark corners.

"You know what I told you," said Jack, as his story ended. He was holding up a book for all to see. "My story was a folk tale told hundreds of years ago in Ghana in Africa. Folk tales not only traveled down through the years. It is interesting to know that they also traveled from country to country. As they traveled, they stayed unchanged in many ways and changed in others. Maybe you know a folk tale which reminds you of Spider. If not, maybe you can find one in this book."

A Folk Tale

When the world we live in
Was very new
And the people in it,
I'm told, were few,
In the firelight
And the starlight
Of a faraway land,
A story began.

From father to son
The story was told
For hundreds of years.
It never grew old.

So now
In much the same way,
In the firelight
And the starlight,
I will tell the same story
To you today.

376

Americans All

Helping Yourself with New Words
Picture Dictionary

bulletin board

magazines

Words You Can Get by Yourself

tell	told	cover	ride	went	thank
retell	untold	discover	wide	sent	blank

Glossary

ei ther (ē′ŦHər), one or the other of two.

en large (en lärj′), to make larger.
      en larged′

his to ry (his′tə rē), a writing or telling about things that have happened.

na tive (nā′tiv), belonging to a country.

num ber (num′bər), the idea used to show order or amount.

sug ges tion (səg jes′chən), an idea for something to do.

cap, fāce, cãre, fär; let, bē, wẻre; it, īce; hot, ōpen, ôrder; voice, house; cut, pùt, tülip, ūse; th, thing; ŦH, then; zh, garage; ə stands for *a* in about, *e* in angel, *i* in cabin, *o* in wagon, *u* in suppose

And So It Ended

Days and weeks had gone by since the morning when Mark Waters had come to school with a world map under his arm. A world map and also a great idea!

Everyone in the room, you remember, was to find out from what country his ancestors had come. Then he was to put his name card on that country. If his mother's ancestors had come from one country and his father's ancestors from another, he needed two cards. Where did a good plan go wrong?

The trouble started with the map. Some countries on the map were so tiny that there was not even room for one name card. Other countries were big enough, but there were so many cards which belonged with each country, that again the plan did not work out as it should. Something had to be done.

Between them, the boys and girls hit upon a better way. The cards were fastened around the edges of the map. A line ran from each card to the country to which it belonged. In the end, this is how the map looked.

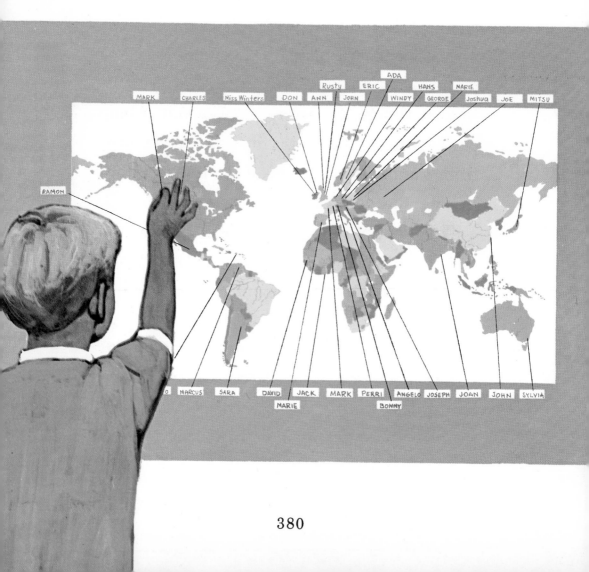

Not every country on the map had a line running to it, but it was surprising how many countries really did.

It was Angelo who got things off to a good start with his story of "Marco and the Donkey Cart." After that everyone had to find something exciting to tell about the country from which his own ancestors had come. It took weeks before everyone had had his turn.

In a book like this, we could not <u>retell</u> ALL the stories about ALL the places from which ALL the ancestors of the boys and girls in Miss Winters's room had come. There was room for only a few. But this you should know. The <u>untold</u> tales were just as exciting as those you have been reading.

When all the cards were fastened to the edges of the map, when all the lines were in and all the stories told, it looked as if things were at an end.

What more was there to do?

There WAS something more and Mark Waters was the one to <u>discover</u> it.

"Something is missing," he almost shouted one morning before school opened, as he stood staring at the supposed-to-be-finished map. "Something is missing and I know what it is."

"But I'M not going to tell any of you," he added, looking around at the boys and girls who had gathered round him. "Not you or Miss Winters <u>either</u>."

"It may take me a few days or even a week or two," Mark went on. "But you'll see. Just you wait and see!"

"Are you goofy?" asked Pedro Gomez, then Windy Chase, then every boy and girl in Room 222. "Nothing is missing! What are you talking about?"

Mark just went on smiling a knowing smile and no one—yes, no one—could pull that secret out of him.

Then things happened just as they had happened on that long ago day when Mark came to school with the map under his arm. About ten days later Mark left for school early one morning. Not one of the Spring Street gang saw him go. Under his arm was a box with something in it. But WHAT?

When the rest of the boys and girls in Room 222 tripped in that morning, there was Mark with a <u>wide</u> grin on his face standing at the side of the map.

Up above the map in a most important place all its own was the picture of a tall, proud-looking Indian boy. Under the picture Mark had painted a sign which read:

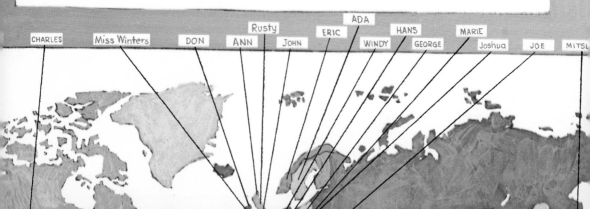

MY ANCESTORS WERE THE FIRST AMERICANS

CHARLES   Miss Winters   DON   ANN   Rusty   JOHN   ERIC   ADA   WINDY   HANS   GEORGE   MARIE   Joshua   JOE   MITSL

"Who is he really? Where did you get that picture?" The chatter, chatter, chatter went on and on and on. Even when Mark tried to explain, he could hardly be heard above all the chatter.

"His name is Sam Woods. I've seen him and talked with him, too. He lives in the North Woods where I went on my last vacation. His home is on the shores of Mystery Lake. I'm going back to visit him this very next summer. When I saw what was missing from our map, I had to write and ask him for a picture. He sent me a little one but my dad had it enlarged for me."

It was hard for Miss Winters to get that room quieted down for work that morning. Again and again she saw the eyes of someone or other fixed on the picture of the proud-looking Indian boy. Maybe she understood. Anyway she did not say anything.

Everyone agreed that the picture was a wonderful finish to the map which hung below it. That Indian boy was where he belonged—in the most important place of all above the map.

You know how one good idea leads to another. It was Windy Chase who came forward with the next suggestion.

"Miss Winters," he said. "If we could use the two big bulletin boards at the back of the room, I have a keen idea."

"That might be arranged," smiled Miss Winters. "I'll think it over. So out with your great idea."

"First," explained Windy, "everyone must bring in a picture of himself. Those pictures can go on one board. Mark can put his small picture of Sam Woods in the middle. The second board will be a harder problem. So I'll wait until our pictures are all up before telling you what to do about that."

It took a while before everyone had found a good picture of himself. The last picture to be clipped to the board was one of Miss Winters.

"Do you know what we all are—all of us?" she asked, as she looked up at the pictures.

Angelo grew so excited that he forgot and threw his book into the air.

"AMERICANS ALL!" he exploded. "That's what we are! Those are the words to go right up there at the top!"

Everyone in Room 222 agreed. Do you?

Windy was right when he said that the second bulletin board would be a much harder problem.

The plan was that every country on the map which had a line running to it should have a picture on the bulletin board to go with it. The picture was to be of someone in native dress who might live in that country—someone dressed in the costume of his native land.

Finding those pictures was a tiresome job, but none of the boys and girls said a word about giving up. They went right on looking in magazines, newspapers, and every place they could think of until they found the needed pictures.

The biggest problem of all was what to do about the Indian boy. There was the little picture of Sam Woods right in the middle of the first bulletin board. Right where it should be. But where did his ancestors come from?

From what country did the American Indians really come? Or did they come from another country after all? Was America their native land? Even the history books didn't seem to have the right answer.

At last David Mays came up with a good suggestion. "Put a blank card the size of Sam's little picture right in the middle of Bulletin Board Number 2. That card will belong to him. It will show that we just don't know."

That seemed to be the best way out for a problem that had no answer.

When all the needed pictures had been found for the second bulletin board, the boys and girls wanted to add the words— MEET OUR ANCESTORS. In the end they agreed on a better name.

FROM FARAWAY PLACES

GLOSSARY

Pronunciation Key

The pronunciation key will help you to understand what the diacritical marks mean in the Glossary of *From Near and Far*.

The principal, or heavy, accent is indicated by the mark ′ after a syllable. In some words another syllable is also accented, but not so heavily. Such a syllable has the mark ′ after it—called a secondary accent.

a as in cap	o as in hot	th as in thing
ā as in fāce	ō as in ōpen	ᴛʜ as in then
ã as in cãre	ô as in ôrder	
ä as in fär		zh as in garage
	oi as in voice	
e as in let	ou as in house	ə represents:
ē as in bē		a in about
ėr as in wėre	u as in cut	e in angel
	u̇ as in pu̇t	i in cabin
i as in it	ü as in tülip	o in wagon
ī as in īce	ū as in ūse	u in suppose

a

ac cuse (ə kūz′), to say that someone has done something wrong. **ac cused′**

Af ri ca (af′rə kə), a continent, one of the large masses of land on the earth.

Af ri can (af′rə kən), of or belonging to the continent of Africa.

a gainst (ə genst′), when compared with; upon.

air (ãr), that which we breathe; the space around us and overhead; a way of acting.

alp (alp), a high mountain.

Alps (alps), the name of the mountains in Switzerland.

al so (ôl′sō), too.

an gry (ang′grē), mad or very much displeased.

ark (ärk), the boat God told Noah to build.

ar rest (ə rest′), to take to jail or court because of wrongdoing. **ar rest′ed**

ar rive (ə riv′), to come to a place. **ar rived′**

art ist (är′tist), one who paints pictures.

aunt (ant), your father's sister, your mother's sister, or your uncle's wife.

b

back ground (bak′ground′), the part of a scene or picture toward the back.

Bal lag ha der een (ba la ha der ēn′), a village.

bar rel (bar′əl), a container with curved sides.

beat (bēt), to hit or pelt; flapped or moved up and down, as wings. **beat′en beat′ing**

bees wax (bēz′waks′), a sticky substance given out by bees, used in making their honeycombs.

be gan (bi gan′), started.

be ret (bə rā′), a round, soft, woolen cap.

bit (bit), a little; to have taken a bite with the teeth.

blank (blangk), having nothing on it, empty.

blond (blond), light-colored.

bon ny (bon′ē), fine.

both (bōth), the two.

brac es (brā′siz), suspenders.

brass (bras), a yellow metal.

break (brāk), to make come to pieces or apart; to stop or put an end to. **break away,** to go away quickly. **break up,** to go different ways. **break′ing**

breath (breth), air drawn into and out of the lungs.

bright (brīt), giving much light, shining; colorful; lively; smart.
bright'er   bright'ly

bright en (brīt'n), to become happy. **bright'ened**

bun dle (bun'dl), things tied together.

burr (bėr), a way of talking in which one trills the letter *r*.

butt (but), to hit with one's head. **but'ted**

c

cal lus (kal'əs), a hardened place on the skin.
cal'lus es

car ry (kar'ē), to hold; to take from one place to another. **carry on,** to act silly. **car'ried**

cart (kärt), a wagon with two wheels.

cat tle (kat'l), cows and bulls.

chap el (chap'l), a small church.

chest (chest), a box with a lid.

child (chīld), a young boy or girl. **chil'dren**

choose (chüz), to select.

clip (klip), to cut short; to put together or fasten with a paper clip or the like. **clipped**

cob bler (kob'lər), a man who fixes shoes.

cock (kok), to turn upward; a rooster. **cocked**

cock y (kok'ē), proud; in love with one's self.

co coa (kō'kō), a drink made from the ground seeds of the cocoa tree.

cold (kōld), not warm; unfriendly.

com bi na tion (kom'bə nā'-shən), two or more people who join to do something together.

com pan ion (kəm pan'yən), a friend who shares in what another is doing.

con tin ue (kən tin'ū), to keep on. **con tin'ued**

cos tume (kos'tüm), a dress or suit.

---

cap, fāce, cāre, fär; let, bē, wėre; it, īce; hot, ōpen, ôrder; voice, house; cut, pùt, tülip, ūse; th, thing; ₮H, then; zh, garage; ə stands for *a* in about, *e* in angel, *i* in cabin, *o* in wagon, *u* in suppose

count (kount), to find out how many; to add up. **count on,** to plan on or figure on something.

count er (koun'tər), a table used for counting money, as in a store.

coun try (kun'trē), all the land of a nation; land where someone was born; land with few houses; from the country.

cow ard (kou'ərd), one who is not brave; one who is afraid.

crack (krak), a small break or opening; to break open. **crack a joke,** to tell a joke. **crack'ing**

crea ture (krē'chər), any living person or animal.

cri (krē), a sea gull's cry.

croak (krōk), a sound made by a frog or a crow. **croak'ing**

cross (krôs), angry, mad; to go across. To cross the fingers or legs is to put one over the other. **crossed cross'ing**

crowd (kroud), a large number of people together; to fill too full; to push close together. **crowd'ed crowd'ing**

cu ri os i ty (kyur'ē os'ə tē), a wish to find out something.

d

dance (dans), to move in time with music; to jump around in a lively way.

dan ger (dān'jər), a thing that may cause harm. **dan'ger ous**

deaf (def), not able to hear.

deck (dek), the floor of a ship.

deep (dēp), thick; far down or back; dark in color; low in sound.

dis ap pear (dis'ə pir'), to go out of sight. **dis'ap peared'**

dis guise (dis giz'), a change in one's looks to hide the way one really looks.

dis gust (dis gust'), a feeling of disliking very much. **dis gust'ed**

drown (droun), to die under water. **drown out,** to keep from being heard. **drowned drown'ing**

Dub lin (dub'lən), a city in Ireland.

e

each (ēch), every one of two or more; every.

earn (ėrn), to do work for something.

ei ther (ē′ᵮHər), one or the other of two.

emp ty (emp′tē), having nothing in it.

en joy (en joi′), to be happy with. **en joyed′ en joy′ing en joy′a ble**

en large (en lärj′), to make larger. **en larged′**

e ven (ē′vən). *Not even* means not as one would expect.

ex cept (ek sept′), but.

ex plode (eks plōd′), to break out with a loud noise. **ex plod′ed**

f

fair (fãr), a gathering of people, goods to sell, games, rides, and so on; doing what is right for everyone.

fast (fast), soon, quick; quickly; to go without food. **fast asleep,** not easily awakened. **stuck fast**, not easily undone.

fa vor ite (fā′vər it), liked better than others.

Fer ris wheel (fer′is hwēl), a large, turning wheel with seats.

few (fū), not many.

fin ish (fin′ish), to do all of the work; to complete. **fin′ished fin′ish ing**

fire en gine (fīr en′jən), an engine for putting out fires.

flash (flash). To do something like a flash is to do it quickly.

folk (fōk), people.

folk tale (fōk tāl), a story made by many people and handed down from father to son.

for est (fôr′ist), deep woods.

four (fôr), one more than three. **on all fours,** on all four feet.

franc (frangk), a coin used in Switzerland.

France (frans), the name of a country.

Franz (fräntz), a man's name.

Fri poun (frē pün′), a sea gull's name.

---

cap, fāce, cãre, fär; let, bē, wėre; it, īce; hot, ōpen, ôrder; voice, house; cut, pùt, tülip, ūse; th, thing; ᵮH, then; zh, garage; ə stands for *a* in about, *e* in angel, *i* in cabin, *o* in wagon, *u* in suppose

g

Gha na (gä′nə), a country in West Africa.

goat skin (gōt′skin′), leather made from the skin of a goat.

grab (grab), to catch hold of. **grabbed**

Gurt (kürt), the name of a cow.

h

half (haf), one of two equal parts; partly.

hear (hir), to pay attention to a sound; to know by sound. **hear′ing**

heard (hėrd), knew by sound; learned.

heav en (hev′ən), the place where God lives.

his to ry (his′tə rē), a writing or telling about things that have happened.

hit (hit), to strike, as with the hand or a stick. **hit upon,** to think of or get to.

hold (hōld), to keep in the hands; to stop; a grip or grasp that keeps something from falling or getting away. **hold back,** to keep from acting. **hold′ing**

hol low (hol′ō), a place shaped like a bowl or cup; rounded and cuplike.

hor ri fy (hôr′ə fī), to shock. **hor′ri fied**

hun dred (hun′drəd), ten tens. **hun′dreds**

hung (hung), fastened to something above.

hun ger (hung′gər), the feeling one has when one needs food. **hun′gry**

hur ry (hėr′ē), to move quickly. **hur′ried**

i

inn (in), a place to eat and spend the night.

in sist (in sist′), to say over and over that something is so. **in sist′ed**

in ter est ing (in′tər is ting), good enough to hold one's attention.

Ire land (īr′lənd), a country.

j

Ja cob (yä′kəb), a man's name.

Ja cot (zhə kō′), the name of a man.

jan i tor (jan′ə tər), one who takes care of a building.

jum bo (jum′bō), very big.

k

knock (nok), to hit. **knocked**
Ko bi (kō′bē), a boy's name.

l

laid (lād), of a bird, gave an
egg; placed.
land lord (land′lôrd′), the
keeper of an inn.
latch (lach), a catch to keep
a door shut without using
a key.
leap (lēp), to jump. **leaped**
lev er (lev′ər), a bar used to
lift something at one end by
pushing down at the other
end.
Lif fey (lif′ē), a river in Ireland.
line (līn), road or track used
by buses or trains; a few
words from a poem or song;
people or things going one
after another; a long mark
drawn on paper.
lot (lot), a number of people
or things. **a lot** or **lots,** a
great many or much.

m

ma gi cian (mə jish′ən),
someone who seems to make
impossible things happen.
man ners (man′ərz), ways of
acting, good or bad.
Mar i (mär′ē), the name of
a woman.
might (mīt), strength or
power to do work; could.
might y (mīt′ē), strong.
miss (mis), to feel the loss
of someone or something;
to not hit, do, meet, or
catch something. **Miss,**
part of the full name of
a single lady.
miss ing (mis′ing), not there.
moun tain eer (mount′n ir′),
one who lives in the mountains.

n

na tive (nā′tiv), belonging
to a country.
nib ble (nib′l), to eat by
taking little bites. **nib′bling**

cap, fāce, cāre, fär; let, bē, wėre; it, īce; hot, ōpen, ôrder; voice, house;
cut, pùt, tülip, ūse; th, thing; ᴛʜ, then; zh, garage; ə stands for a in about,
e in angel, i in cabin, o in wagon, u in suppose

No ah (nō′ə), the man in the Bible whom God told to build the ark.

nod (nod), to bend the head a little and then raise it again. **nod′ded**

none (nun), not any.

num ber (num′bər), the idea used to show order or amount.

p

pa rade (pə rād′), to march or walk with others in a long line. **pa rad′ed**

ped dler (ped′lər), one who travels around, selling things.

pelt (pelt), to beat or hit. **pelt′ed pelt′ing**

place (plās), to put; a part of a space or spot taken up by something or someone. **in the first place,** first of all. **placed**

po lice man (pə lēs′mən), one who keeps order and sees that laws are not broken.

prob lem (prob′ləm), something to be worked out.

pro tect (prə tekt′), to keep from harm. **pro tect′ing**

push (pu̇sh), to move something by pressing against it; to press. **push′er pushed**

q

quick (kwik), fast. **quick′ly**

qui et (kwī′ət), still. **qui′et ly**

r

re tell (rē tel′), to tell again.

rice (rīs), a plant grown in warm countries; the seeds of this plant.

ring (ring), to put a ring around; to make an edge around; to sound, as a bell; a trinket for the finger; a circle or edge. **ringed ring′ing**

ring-of-day, daybreak, dawn.

rob ber (rob′ər), one who steals.

rus ty (rus′tē), covered with a reddish-brown coating.

s

sab ot (sä bō′), a shoe made of one piece of wood.

sar dine (sär dēn′), a small fish.

sat is fy (sat′is fī), to give one enough of what he wants. **sat′is fied sat′is fy ing**

Scot land (skot′lənd), the name of a country.

sec ond (sek′ənd), a very short time; the next one after first; time.

sent (sent), made to be carried from one place to another.

Sepp (sep), a boy's name.

shep herd (shep′ərd), a man who takes care of sheep.

shil ling (shil′ing), a piece of money worth about 14 cents.

short (shôrt), not tall; not long; cut down from a longer name.

shoul der (shōl′dər), the part of the body to which the arms are fastened.

sign (sīn), a move of the hand, a sound, a picture or something else that has a special meaning.

sil ver (sil′vər), a shining white metal.

sis ter (sis′tər), a daughter of your mother and father; a name sometimes used in place of a girl's real name.

six pence (siks′pəns), a piece of money worth about 7 pennies.

smooth (smüŦH), flat; level.

soft-heart ed (sôft′här′tid), kind.

son (sun), a boy child of his mother and father; a name sometimes used in place of a boy's real name.

speak (spēk), to say words; talk; say. **speak′er**

squawk (skwôk), a loud, unpleasing sound.
squawked   squawk′ing

stall (stôl), a small place for selling things.

stat ue (stach′ü), a carved likeness of someone.

steal (stēl), to take something that belongs to someone else; to sneak, to move very quietly. **steal′ing**

steep (stēp), almost straight up and down.

stom ach (stum′ək), a belly.

stone deaf (stōn′def′), entirely deaf.

strange (strānj), queer; not often found.

---

cap, fāce, cāre, fär; let, bē, wėre; it, īce; hot, ōpen, ôrder; voice, house; cut, pùt, tülip, ūse; th, thing; ŦH, then; zh, garage; ə stands for *a* in about, *e* in angel, *i* in cabin, *o* in wagon, *u* in suppose

stretch (strech), to pull out and make longer. **stretched**

stu pid (stü'pid), not wise; a know-nothing.

sug ges tion (səg jes'chən), an idea for something to do.

swamp (swomp), wet, soft ground.

Switz er land (swit'sər lənd), the name of a country.

t

tale (tāl), a story.

taste (tāst), to take a small bite of.

tast y (tās'tē), good or pleasing to eat.

there a bouts (ᴛHãr'ə bouts'), near that place.

thief (thēf), one who steals.

thieve (thēv), to steal.
     thiev'ing

third (thėrd), next after the second.

thought (thôt), had in mind; used the mind; idea.

through (thrü), between the parts of.

thumb (thum), the short, thick finger of a hand.

Tim o thy (tim'ə thē), a boy's name.

tore (tôr), ripped or pulled; hurried.

toss (tôs), to throw lightly.

trail (trāl), path.

trav el (trav'l), to go from one place to another.
     trav'el er   **trav'eled**
       trav'el ing

treas ure (trezh'ər), something worth much; riches.

trin ket (tring'kit), a ring or other bit of jewelry, not worth much.

true (trü), telling of something that is real. **came true,** became real.

turf (tėrf), dry grass and roots, used for burning.

twen ty (twen'tē), two times ten.

twice (twīs), two times.

u

um brel la (um brel'ə), a cloth-covered frame carried to keep rain or sun from hitting the body.

un told (un tōld'), not told.

v

val ley (val'ē), a low place between hills.

veg e ta ble (vej'tə bl), a plant used for food.

vest (vest), a short, sleeveless coat.

w

waist (wāst), the middle part of the body.

wave (wāv), to move something, as the hand, up and down or from side to side; moving water; to move as a wave of water does.
waved wav′ing

wear (wãr), to have on one's body.

wea ry (wir′ē), tired.

which (hwich), a question word; a connecting word; the one that; the thing that.

wide (wīd), long from side to side.

wom an (wùm′ən), a lady, a grown-up girl.

wrench (rench), a tool for turning nuts and bolts.
monkey wrench, a wrench with a jaw that can be moved to fit different sizes of nuts.

wring (ring), to twist.

y

yowl (youl), a long, sad cry.
yowl′ing

cap, fāce, cãre, fär; let, bē, wėre; it, īce; hot, ōpen, ôrder; voice, house; cut, pùt, tülip, ūse; th, thing; ₮ʜ, then; zh, garage; ə stands for *a* in about, *e* in angel, *i* in cabin, *o* in wagon, *u* in suppose